ECSTASY AS MEDICINE

How MDMA Therapy Can Help You Overcome
Trauma, Anxiety, and Depression
...and Feel More Love

JONATHAN ROBINSON

Free Resources for You:

If you'd like to be on my email list and receive my blog, go to:
XTCasMedicine.com
And put in your email address. You will immediately gain
access to 12 questions for Instant Intimacy with anyone,
AND 10 ways to avoid bad psychedelic experiences,
AND info on my next MDMA facilitation training
(including a discount code)

WHAT PEOPLE SAY ABOUT
ECSTASY AS MEDICINE

"This is an authoritative, comprehensive, and highly practical guide to optimizing the potential therapeutic benefit of MDMA."

–Michael Horwitz, MD
Former Director of Addiction Medicine, Cedars-Sinai Medical Center

"This book is destined to be an instant classic. In it, Jonathan shares the most powerful tools and understandings he's gathered from over 40 years of MDMA therapy with thousands of clients. If you want a complete and detailed understanding of how MDMA therapy can change your life, you'll want to read this."

–Ted Strauss,
Co-author *iConscious - Accelerating Human Potential*

Jonathan Robinson provides not only an overview of the research on MDMA-assisted therapy, but many personal stories from people who have benefited from this treatment. He also discusses the risks and benefits of MDMA, its legal status, and the road ahead for patients and therapists alike. There is no individual better suited to writing a book on this subject, and he has done a masterful job."

– Jonathan Brian Evans,
MD, MBA, FACEP, CPE

"Jonathan accomplished, in one session, what six years of intense talk therapy could not solve. The insights I had were life-changing. What a blessing!"

–Marilyn Van Derbur,
Former Miss America, incest survivor, author of *Miss America By Day*

TABLE OF CONTENTS

AUTHOR'S NOTE AND DISCLAIMER

While the author provides much information about the drug known as MDMA, Ecstasy, or Molly, his material is not meant to mean he is advocating for its use. Buying or ingesting any illegal substance is risky, and such substances often consist of unknown chemical makeup and purity. In this book, the author tries to educate readers on how to reduce the possible risks associated with the use of medically prescribed MDMA—which is currently legal or decriminalized in some countries. Providing risk reduction information should not be interpreted as encouragement to use or abuse any legal or illicit substance. The author is not responsible for any adverse effects or consequences resulting from the use of any of the suggestions or procedures discussed in this book. As of this writing, in late 2023, MDMA is a Schedule I illegal drug in the United States. This puts MDMA in the same category as marijuana, heroin, and LSD. Therefore, readers are cautioned to consult appropriate criminal law and medicine experts about the risks of ingesting MDMA before deciding to do so.

DEDICATION

To Rick Doblin and my teachers Justin Gold, Ram Dass, and Dr. Jeffery Martin, as well as all of the people who aim to use psychedelics in a healing manner.

INTRODUCTION

MDMA, often called Ecstasy or Molly, is an amazing medicine. For thousands of years, human beings have sought simple and safe ways to open their hearts and see their lives from an expanded perspective. MDMA is possibly the most effective medicine ever created for helping people tap into their innermost wisdom, joy, and love.

In the last 40 years, I've led MDMA journeys with perhaps 600 individuals and 150 couples. Due to the drug being illegal during this period, I've had to keep my research and observations under the radar. Now that MDMA and psychedelics are becoming more accepted—and even gaining legal status in some places–I am more open about what I've learned.

Besides conducting MDMA-assisted therapy, many people know me as someone who has been a frequent guest on *Oprah*, a bestselling author of 14 books, and the co-host of a popular podcast called "Awareness Explorers." While I've been able to accomplish much, my desire to succeed was largely a reaction to feeling like a powerless victim in my childhood. My stepfather used to beat me up regularly, and there was a lot of dysfunction in my family. As a result of my family dynamics, I often felt sad, anxious, and afraid.

Since I couldn't leave my family, starting at age 12, I looked for what could help me heal my pain and psychological issues. Over time, I tried many things, from self-help books to yoga and meditation, to LSD. Yet, the first time I tried MDMA, I knew I had stumbled upon something that could profoundly help me. This medicine has changed my life, and with its help, I've been able to change the lives of the many people I've worked with.

My experience researching MDMA dates to when I was a psychology graduate student at U.C. Santa Barbara in 1984. For my Master's thesis, I legally gave MDMA to 36 people who suffered from Post-Traumatic Stress Disorder (PTSD). While they were on the drug, I counseled them about their trauma. Of the 36 people I worked with, 34 said their PTSD symptoms were "completely or mostly gone" six months after a single journey. These results astounded my supervisor. He wanted me to do the study again to ensure my results were valid. By that time, however, the U.S. government had made the drug illegal, and no more research could be conducted. Fortunately, that has begun to change.

Recently, in an online course I teach on how to do MDMA facilitation, I've taught hundreds of therapists how to guide medicine journeys effectively. My class has over 25 hours of video lectures and involves practicing many specific skills. There is a lot to know to facilitate MDMA journeys successfully. However, in this book, I've included just the most practical and essential information you need to know if you're considering trying this type of therapy. In addition, if you ever plan to help a lover, a friend, or a client with their journey, the material in this book will be invaluable.

As of this writing in late 2023, MDMA is expected to become an FDA-approved medically prescribed drug sometime in 2024. Never in U.S. history has a Schedule 1 illegal drug gained FDA approval and become a legal medicine. Why is this happening? Because decades of clinical trials indicate MDMA is very safe and effective for treating everything from trauma, anxiety, and depression, to addiction and social isolation. In addition, unlike psilocybin and LSD, people don't hallucinate on MDMA–and bad "trips" are almost unheard of.

In my career, I always try to reveal the best, easiest, and most powerful psychological and spiritual growth methods. In my experience, MDMA therapy is in a class by itself. In a single session, people often make breakthroughs that, with some integration work afterward, have a profound impact on the rest of their lives. Whether you're seeking help finding inner peace, a better relationship, or support overcoming a psychological challenge, MDMA-assisted therapy can be miraculously effective. I hope the ideas and methods I've learned over the years with MDMA can be just as transformative for you.

In Part I of this book, I reveal the latest research and cutting-edge ways of using MDMA, along with some history and caveats about its use. In Part II, I dive into how various methods in conjunction with MDMA can lead to breakthroughs in conditions such as PTSD, anxiety, depression, and couple issues. In Part III, I explore powerful ways the insights and changes brought on by an MDMA journey can be integrated into transforming one's daily life.

We all want more joy, peace, and love in our lives. When taken under favorable conditions, MDMA is a sacred medicine that can help you connect with your deep wisdom, open-heartedness, and self-healing abilities. It is truly a gift to humanity. By reading this book, I hope you'll be well prepared for how you might engage with MDMA. In the crazy times in which we live, we all could use the best ways to tap into more love, healing, and connection…

PART I

PROVEN THERAPY
AND NEW POSSIBILITIES

In this section, I cover some of the research and history of MDMA, including the results of placebo-controlled studies with this medicine. In addition, I describe how I and many guides structure MDMA and other psychedelic-assisted sessions. You'll learn why it's so effective, various options for its use, and things to avoid when pursuing this type of therapy.

"So I'm guessing we're in the placebo group."

CHAPTER 1

THE BREAKTHROUGH
MEDICINE AND PROTOCOL

"MDMA shows us that the boundaries between ourselves and others are an illusion. We are all connected, and love is the ultimate truth."

-Timothy Leary, former Harvard professor

MDMA is truly a breakthrough medicine. Don't just take my word for it. In 2017 the U.S. Food and Drug Administration [FDA] granted Breakthrough Therapy designation to MDMA-assisted psychotherapy for treating PTSD. This designation helps expedite the development and review of drugs that are shown to be extremely promising for treating a serious condition. As years of MDMA clinical trials finish, it has been shown to be one of the most effective pharmacological drugs ever created.

I first came upon MDMA as a graduate student in psychology. I had heard it created a nice "high," but the experience was so much more. When I tried MDMA, I felt like it created a window into my heart, and a new hope for what could be possible for me in my life. Unlike LSD and psilocybin "magic" mushrooms, MDMA didn't feel like a drug.

Instead, it felt like I was experiencing the best, most loving version of myself. My experience is not uncommon. In fact, my dad and step-mother once asked me if they could try this drug I was raving about. I supplied it to them and then gave them directions for creating a good setting for their journey. A year later, I asked them if they had taken it. They told me they had indeed ingested the drug but reported that "it had no effect." Surprised by their statement, I asked them, "So, what *exactly* happened after you took the medicine?"

What my parents reported next had me laughing for a long time. They said, "Well, once we got over the fact that the drug didn't work, we sat on the couch and talked about how wonderful our lives were. We chatted about how lucky we were to be so in love with each other after all these years. We felt especially grateful for our house, kids, and careers. Then, after talking about the purpose of our lives for a couple of hours, we just cuddled on the couch. Despite the drug not working, it was perhaps the best night of our 30-year marriage!" ...Somehow, my parents had totally missed realizing the drug had facilitated this experience for them.

I asked my parents, "When was the last time you talked about your love for each other for several hours, then cuddled on the couch?" Of course, they answered, "Well, that has never happened before." Nevertheless, they still insisted they were not under the influence of a drug! Such can be the experience of MDMA. At low and even medium dosages, MDMA can have a profound effect while simultaneously feeling per-fectly natural. For many people, its most noticeable features are not wild hallucinations or significant changes in character. Instead, people sim-ply notice an absence of anxiety, an openness to the present moment, and a desire to connect authentically with others. That's why it has often been called the "love drug" or the "hug drug."

When I asked people to describe what taking MDMA the first time was like for them, here are some of the comments I received:

"Mentally, you feel like your first crush is kissing you. All pure innocence and true love."

"Once it started taking effect, I became more talkative, and my mind seemed to open up, allowing me to think about things I normally wouldn't have. I could see things differently, from a different point of view. It was like waking up to true mental clarity."

"I felt a new kind of energy frothing up inside me, coursing through my body like champagne bubbles. This was wonderful! And it felt so good!"

"I smiled the biggest smile of my life. Looking at myself smiling back at myself, I felt like a little infant just smiling for the sheer joy of being."

"This was a huge turning point for me, as I had forgotten what it was like to be really, really happy and relaxed. I had become resigned to spending the rest of my life in some low emotional flatland. Now I realized just how depressed I had been. I realized that this effortless ecstasy was the state I was really seeking to be in. This was the real deal."

"I had suffered from PTSD for 12 years, but after the MDMA session, I had no more symptoms. None. And the best part is it also helped me embrace more joy. It was actually fun to do the session. I didn't expect it would be so much fun."

"As my partner and I regained our close, loving contact, we had the deepest mutual understanding we had experienced in years. We spoke some important truths to each other, all honestly intended and lovingly received. Some heavy baggage of recent years had fallen away. It was miraculous."

As you just read, MDMA can create magic in people's lives in as little as a single day. Although I usually guide clients on this medicine for just a single session, I'll occasionally guide them in a second or even third session several weeks apart. I do this because each time a person takes MDMA, they might focus on a different theme or intention. The four most common themes that arise during a journey are:

1. Issues around trauma and a lessening of anxiety.

2. Opening to more joy, love, and happiness in daily life.

3. Evaluation of one's life, career, and upcoming significant decisions.

4. Improving a relationship with a friend, lover, or family member.

Sometimes, all four themes can be attended to in a single session, and sometimes not. But whatever is explored during a journey, it always feels like an honor to guide someone through a personal transformation.

The MAPS Protocol

Once MDMA was made illegal in the United States in 1985, research into its therapeutic potential basically stopped for many years. I'll briefly go into the history of MDMA in Chapter 3, but for now, suffice it to say that an organization called MAPS was created to help eventually make MDMA a legally prescribed medicine. MAPS stands for **M**ulti-disciplinary **A**ssociation for **P**sychedelic **S**tudies. MAPS has been instrumental in creating a specific protocol for using MDMA as a therapeutic medicine—and financing studies for seeking FDA approval.

In their clinical trials, MAPS had to decide on a specific protocol to conduct MDMA-assisted therapy. Their protocol aims to provide a safe and effective framework for therapeutic sessions. Their process begins with thoroughly screening potential participants to ensure their suitability for the therapy. Then, the core of the MAPS protocol involves a series of three MDMA-assisted therapy sessions. Each session typically takes place eight weeks apart and consists of a full-day experience. The therapy is administered by a trained co-therapy team, which includes a male and a female therapist.

The MAPS-sponsored sessions are conducted primarily using a non-directive approach, allowing the participant to guide their experience. Before a client's first journey–and between journeys– they meet with a therapist to discuss their issues. However, during the actual MDMA journeys, the therapists mainly provide empathic support and gentle guidance when requested. Calming and supportive music is played during the session to facilitate reflection and emotional expression. Participants typically wear a blindfold to enhance their internal focus. At the end of the session, the client is encouraged to spend time integrating their experience with such things as journaling and contemplation.

Using this basic protocol, the results were quite incredible. In Phase 3 clinical trials conducted by the FDA, 88% of participants with severe PTSD experienced a clinically significant reduction in PTSD. Additionally, 67% of participants in the MDMA group (compared to 32% of participants in the placebo group) no longer met the criteria for PTSD two months after the sessions.[1] For people studying the effects of pharmacological medicines, these results were mind-blowing. After all, anti-depressants, a multi-billion dollar-a-year industry, have often been shown to be only 1% more effective than placebos for people with mild or moderate depression.[2] In contrast, clinical trials indicated that MDMA was 35% more effective than the placebo-controlled group.

Despite the proven value of the MAPS protocol, I use a very different approach in my work with clients. Over the last four decades, I've developed a protocol that seems to create as good or even better results

---

[1] https://maps.org/mdma/ptsd/phase3/
[2] https://www.frontiersin.org/articles/10.3389/fpsyt.2019.00407/full

in much less time--and potentially at a fraction of the cost of using the MAPS approach. In all fairness, the MAPS trials used participants with severe PTSD, whereas my clientele has tended to be more varied. Nevertheless, the results I've received over 40 years when using just a single MDMA session have been so spectacular that even *I* can barely believe it.

I think the reason my results have become so good is that I've continually "tinkered" with my protocol to maximize beneficial results. Over several decades, I've kept what worked and disregarded what seemed unnecessary. This has resulted in a highly streamlined approach that, despite my not doing clinical trials to offer proof, seems to get consistently great results. Unfortunately, MAPS has been unable to tinker with its approach over the years. Doing so would mean they'd have to start over with their clinical trials—which takes millions of dollars and many years to do. So, they're effectively fixed with what they decided was a good approach long ago. Don't get me wrong. The MAPS protocol is exceptionally effective–even for people with severe PTSD; it's just rather prolonged and will be very expensive when it gets FDA approval.

In the MAPS protocol, a minimal amount of actual talk therapy is conducted while a patient is on MDMA. To get FDA approval, it was important to show that a simple pill could significantly help people. However, it has been my experience that MDMA, in combination with cutting-edge therapy methods, yields even better outcomes. Nevertheless, the fact that the MAPS protocol will almost certainly get FDA approval gives credence to their persistence and their approach.

My Latest Protocol

By now, you may be wondering what makes my less expensive and faster approach as good or better than the time-tested ways of the MAPS organization. Basically, I do five things differently. First, instead of doing three MDMA sessions several weeks apart, I generally do just a single session. Why? Because if you tell folks they get three sessions, they will often wait to improve during the third session. If, on the other hand, you tell folks they get one session to overcome their challenge, they tend to change in just a single session. Of course, this single-session therapy dramatically reduces the cost of this type of work. In addition, the fact that my protocol involves only a single therapist—and not two—makes my approach much less expensive. I should add that, with complex or severe cases, I *will* see some clients for a second (or even third) session, but only when necessary, and it is rarely necessary.

A second thing I've done differently than the MAPS protocol is I do almost all my sessions over Zoom. I imagine you're either shocked or denigrating that I do most of my journey work over Zoom. Of course, it wasn't always this way. Before the Covid pandemic, I did sessions in my office. Yet, once the pandemic hit, there were a lot of folks feeling traumatized and needing help, so I thought I'd try to lead a journey over Zoom. To my amazement, it worked. In fact, I'd have to say that the 250 sessions I've done over Zoom seem to get even better results than the ones I formally did in person! For added safety, I require the client to have a friend nearby in case they need additional support, but that has never been needed. In addition, I should add that I don't lead any other type of psychedelic journeys over Zoom—just MDMA. I find that all the other psychedelics are just too unpredictable and are not safe enough to lead without being physically present.

People often ask me why I might be getting better results with MDMA over Zoom. It is indeed an interesting phenomenon. Since I don't have millions of dollars to do a scientific study about it, I can only speculate. My guess is that a major reason MDMA therapy over Zoom is so effective is because it creates a feeling of extreme safety, thus helping folks to look at their issues fearlessly. Studies show that MDMA reduces activity in the amygdala part of the brain, which is activated when we feel fear. Going to a stranger's office and taking a drug may not be the best setting for helping people feel safe. On the other hand, when sessions are conducted over Zoom, a client is safely and comfortably in their own home. While safely in their home, the MDMA medicine creates the ultimate feeling of safety. From such a feeling, the therapeutic process works amazingly well.

A third feature of my journey work different from the MAPS protocol is that I tend to be more directive. As you'll read in future chapters, I use various therapeutic methods with my clients while they are on the drug. In contrast, therapists using the MAPS protocol mostly listen to their participants with little direction. Occasionally, they ask the participant a question or offer empathic support. However, in a MAPS session, clients mostly spend their time lying down with a blindfold and listening to music. While clinical trials show the MAPS method to be quite effective, I believe it doesn't make full use of the therapeutic potential of MDMA. When I have a client on MDMA, I find that with the help of some therapeutic interventions, I can accomplish about two years of therapy in a single day.

Once again, you may be skeptical that so much can be accomplished so quickly—especially over Zoom. Fortunately, while on MDMA, clients seem to have no problem staying focused and looking at a screen for five hours. *I'm* the one that usually requests a "stretch break" every now and then. Although I offer my clients the option that they can lie down and wear a blindfold–as in the MAPS protocol–virtually none of my clients choose to do so. Instead, they want to dive deep into their issues and explore with my help. On the medicine, they find such work to be very satisfying and extremely effective. One client reported, "It was like the best therapy session of my life, but on steroids. Working through all my stuff in a few hours was extremely satisfying."

A fourth aspect of my protocol outside the MAPS method is that I have my client audio record (via their smartphone) the entire journey. In my sessions, there are a lot of interventions and explorations between me and my client. Therefore, the recording is full of critical insights and information. Many of my clients have said listening to the four-to-five-hour recording was as powerful as the actual session. The recording seems to reinforce what was learned and give clients a clear sense of their path forward. I require that clients listen to the recording before we conduct our integration session. Because they've listened to their entire journey on audio, my clients have a good sense of what to focus on during our integration session.

A fifth and final difference between the MAPS protocol and my own is that I have developed a specific integration process that is marvelously effective. I believe the integration session I do—approximately a week after the journey—is as important as the actual MDMA session. In this one-hour Zoom call, I go over key insights and experiences that occurred during the journey work. We then devise a plan to integrate their key insights and new behaviors into their daily lives. Finally, I give my clients an extremely powerful motivational method that allows them to do the actions they know would improve their lives consistently. (Part III of this book fully details my integration methodology). The result is that clients can quickly overcome challenges that had eluded them previously.

Mary came to me suffering from a multitude of psychological challenges. She complained she had trauma, anxiety, *and* depression and had "tried everything, but nothing has helped." After Mary filled-out a form asking detailed questions about her past, we set a date for the MDMA therapy over Zoom. As soon as the medicine took effect, it was as if a new person appeared. She was calm, wise, open, and eager to look at her internal obstacles to peace. She dove into some tough places but came out shining and joyous by the end of the session. A week later, we created a specific plan for how to effectively deal with her issues–based on her insights from the journey. When I checked in with Mary three months later, she said, "You gave me a new life. I'm no longer anxious or depressed. There is still work to do, but I can see how much progress I've made each week. My only regret is that I didn't do this thirty years ago."

The Key Ingredients

My clients have often been surprised by the results they receive. Many of them have previously gone through many years of different therapies with little to show for it. When they ask me why the protocol I've developed is so effective, I tell them many ingredients make it work so well.

First, the MDMA medicine is truly a breakthrough drug. It creates a safe and open feeling that makes therapeutic work easy, effective, and profound. A second key is that I do an initial (non-drug) session in which the client's intention and desired results are greatly clarified. It's easier to hit a target if you know what the target is. By knowing exactly what the client defines as a successful outcome, I can better direct my interventions to create the result they desire.

A third reason the protocol I use is so effective is because it (usually) involves only a single session. People have an easier time changing quickly—rather than slowly over time. The normal model of going to a therapist for many weeks or years is actually quite ineffective–except in extreme cases. Such an approach tends to lead to putting off important changes. Instead, my system indirectly announces that *today* is the time to make a shift in your life. The protocol I use gives folks a clear ultimatum: face your issues head-on today—because there will not be another MDMA session (except in rare cases). As Yoda (of Star Wars fame) once said, "Do or do not. There is no try." By giving folks a clear "deadline" for a change or insight to occur, they typically rise to the occasion.

The final reason I get such good results has to do with motivation. I've developed a unique method that keeps folks motivated over a long period of time. While a shift in one's life can indeed happen quickly, in most cases, there is a need to be consistent with some new behavior.

With my motivation method, clients can consistently act on their new insights in a way that was impossible without this method. However, I should add that perhaps 5% of folks don't get much benefit from their journey. Usually, this is because they choose to do something other than the motivation method I suggest and therefore fall back to their old ways. (Once again, the motivation and integration methods I created will be explained in detail in Part III of this book.)

In an accelerated world, we all could use better ways to adapt to our ever-shifting lives. I believe that MDMA-assisted therapy and the unique protocol I've developed provide a faster, less expensive, and more effective way to help people overcome psychological challenges. Of course, no approach to helping people feels right or works for everyone. Each person is unique. Therefore, different people will benefit from diverse approaches. Yet, MDMA-assisted therapy that is directive, done over Zoom, and includes a motivational strategy for maintaining change is, in my opinion, a breakthrough remedy for a variety of issues that people face. As you'll read in the remaining chapters, it may be what you need to create a transformation in your own life.

CHAPTER 2

CONCERNS AND CONTRAINDICATIONS

"Just say 'no' to drugs. Although if you're talking to drugs, you may already be on drugs."

— George Carlin, comedian

By now, you're hopefully sold on the idea that MDMA-assisted therapy can be a valuable, even life-transforming experience. But there's always a catch. Fortunately, the challenges with this type of therapy can be overcome if you know the correct information. I'll provide as much of that information as possible here. However, before reading this chapter, I want to warn you of some things. First, this chapter is not meant to be entertaining–and I think you'll agree I've succeeded with that intention! It aims to inform you of possible concerns or contraindications about MDMA therapy–and how to overcome them. Even if you're a seasoned user of this medicine, I advise you to read about the various precautions I detail here. It could remind you of things you may have overlooked or not been aware of. Of course, if you don't know much about the potential downsides of the use of MDMA, the information that follows is doubly essential.

The challenges associated with MDMA therapy fall into six basic categories. I label these six categories: the cost, getting pure medicine, contraindications for this type of therapy, finding a qualified guide, dealing with unpleasant side effects, and potential legal issues. I'll tackle each challenge in turn.

The Cost:

First, there is the cost. The drug itself is not very expensive. It is often sold for between $15 and $30 per dose. Yet, if you want a trained MDMA facilitator guide, that can get pricey. When MDMA becomes a medically prescribed drug, a few clinics that use the MAPS protocol with highly trained therapists will pop up. Unfortunately, the MAPS protocol requires three MDMA sessions with two therapists and additional talk therapy before each session. That means it will likely cost a small fortune. Although such clinics don't yet exist, I've read that the cost will probably be between $10,000 and $15,000. That's the bad news. The good news is that, at some point, insurance companies will likely pay for a large percentage of that cost—especially for people with PTSD.

Of course, I and hundreds of other people have been doing MDMA-assisted therapy for many years in a non-legal, "underground" market. While the costs for such services vary depending on who the therapist is, it's common for guides to use a protocol similar to mine and charge between $600 and $2500. Considering that this type of treatment can be like doing years of therapy in a single day, that's a very reasonable fee. I think it's a great bargain because two years of weekly therapy would take a lot of time, cost you well over $10,000, and might not achieve as good a result.

The Medicine:

Next is the challenge of securing the medicine. At a legal clinic (when they arise), they would supply the MDMA. Yet, when working with an underground guide, they may or may not provide the medicine. If they don't, or if your session is over Zoom, you'll have to find a way to get pure MDMA. With folks I work with, I give them the name of a contact I have that can supply them with pure medicine at a reasonable price. My connection uses a fully encrypted messaging app called Signal, and thus this offers them the added protection that their communications over the app are not traceable by law enforcement. My clients order MDMA from my contact, pay for it in an agreed-upon manner, and my contact mails them the goods. While there is always a legal risk in working with an illegal Schedule 1 substance, I have not ever experienced or heard of any legal trouble stemming from this approach. However, every guide should make the disclaimer to their client that, while the legal risk may be very low, MDMA (as of late 2023) is still an illegal substance and there is some amount of legal risk.

It should be noted that if you get MDMA from a connection you do not know well, testing it for purity is essential. Nowadays, dealers often sell what they say is MDMA, but it is sometimes mixed with other things—such as methamphetamine or bath salts. If you're concerned, there are two things you can do. First, you can ask if anyone else has tried the batch you're considering trying, and if so, can you talk to them? Someone who has used the same batch can probably tell you if the stuff you're considering trying is real MDMA. Second, you can buy a test kit to see if the MDMA you have is pure MDMA or if it's mixed with other stuff that might lead to a bad trip. Here's a link to a test kit you can buy: https://dancesafe.org/product/mdma-testing-kit/. It costs $50, and it will do over 50 tests.

Another option, which is important to do, is to test your MDMA for Fentanyl. As you probably know, Fentanyl is a highly dangerous opioid that kills many people each year. Although it is rarely found in MDMA, it has been known to occur. For peace of mind, I suggest testing any new MDMA source you secure for traces of Fentanyl. Fortunately, you can buy a Fentanyl "test-strip" that's highly accurate for a mere $1.99 at this site: https://dancesafe.org/product-category/testing-strips/

Contraindications:

Not everyone is suitable for MDMA-assisted therapy. The most frequent impediments are other medications that, when combined with MDMA, either lessen its effects or make it dangerous. First, there is a class of drugs known as MAO inhibitors. Most of these medications are anti-depressant or anti-anxiety medicines. Common names for them include Marplan, Nardil, Emsam, and Parnate. These medicines aren't as common as they once were because safer treatments have largely replaced them. Yet, I always ask prospective clients if they are taking any prescribed medicines, and I ask specifically about MAOIs drugs because they can be dangerous when combined with MDMA.

A more frequent obstacle to MDMA therapy is when a client takes an SSRI anti-depressant. Common names for these types of anti-depressants include Lexapro, Prozac, Zoloft, Paxil, Celexa, and many others. Since new anti-depressants are always coming out, I suggest you Google any medicine you take to see if it is an SSRI-type drug. If it is, it can interfere with you feeling the effects of MDMA because such medications work on the same neurotransmitter pathway. In addition, on extremely rare occasions combining MDMA with an SSRI drug can cause something called Serotonin Syndrome—which can be dangerous. If you want an entire article that explains more about all this, you can find that here: https://www.vice.com/en/article/padgjm/everything-you-need-to-know-about-mixing-mdma-and-antidepressants-safe-sesh

Since many clients who come to me are also on SSRIs, I have established a way of handling such cases. Typically, I suggest that if they want to do MDMA therapy, they should work with their doctor to reduce the dosage of their anti-depressant over a two-or three-month period.

If they agree to that, we then plan an MDMA session for two or three months hence. Of course, clients may sometimes find that reducing their anti-depressant medicine feels too uncomfortable. In such cases, I wish them well and we cancel their planned MDMA session. Yet, in many instances, I've had a client slightly reduce the dosage of their anti-depressant medicine–then still partake in their MDMA journey. For these clients, I start them at a somewhat higher dose than average (160 mg instead of 120mg). Then, an hour into their session, if they feel they want more effect, they take a 60mg booster. However, before trying such a regimen, or leading someone on such a regimen, I suggest you discuss it with a doctor who has experience in this area.

Although I only have a small amount of experience with clients taking MDMA while on SSRIs, I've never encountered a problem with this approach. Unfortunately, there is negligible research on how safe or valuable this approach is. The main drawback I've seen is that, when taking a small dose of anti-depressants, clients may react less to the MDMA than someone not on such medicine. Therefore, it can be helpful for such people to have a 60 mg booster dose of MDMA available if needed. Once again, because there is not much research in this area, you may want to do your own research and determine for yourself if the potential benefits are worth the potential risks involved.

Since new information is always coming out, I strongly suggest you do your own research when it comes to combining any anti-depressants with MDMA. All you need to do is type into Google the name of any medication you take, along with the letters MDMA, and you'll see articles about possible contraindications show up. Regrettably, such reports are often written in scientific jargon so removed from English that it may be hard to know what they're actually trying to say. Yet, if you read carefully, you can ascertain if the study says that combining MDMA with your prescription meds *might* cause a problem–or if it says they should not be combined under any circumstances. Ultimately, you and/

or your client must decide what level of risk you're willing to take. For most people, the biggest problem with taking MDMA while on anti-depressants is that the effect is somewhat muted.

Finding a Qualified Guide

For people looking to try MDMA therapy for the first time, finding a qualified guide can be a challenge. If you are a licensed therapist seeking to provide guidance in therapy, I encourage you to check out my training program at MDMAtraining.net. If you are an individual reading this book who seeks a qualified guide, feel free to contact me at: info@XTCasMedicine.com for a referral to someone I've trained and that I vouch for in my network. I have trained hundreds of people to do MDMA facilitation, and I often make referrals to guides that I think are especially good at what they do. While most people I've trained also work primarily on Zoom, many also see clients in their home or office. If you prefer to work with a guide in person, I can often refer you to someone who lives in or near your area.

Since an MDMA therapy session is a rather intimate experience, it's important that you feel safe and trust whoever you use to guide you. While some individuals may consider using a trusted friend or partner as a guide, I would heartily recommend someone trained in such guidance. The feeling of trust you have with your guide, along with their skills, dramatically impacts the result you're likely to experience. I often hear from my clients that being guided by me (or someone else who is trained) is an entirely different experience than when taking MDMA with a friend.

You may also choose to do an MDMA session alone, with only yourself as a guide. I have devoted Chapter 13 to this option. The main problem with a self-guided session is that it's quite difficult to do well. The MDMA medicine tends to induce a state of euphoria, and most folks have trouble diving into challenging issues or focusing on insights when feeling so good—unless they have a guide. If you're considering self-guided therapy, I'll provide many helpful pointers about how best to do that in Chapter 13.

I have a friend, Mike, who has done self-guided MDMA trips for years. He often told me about them and the great value he received from these journeys. One day, I suggested he do a session in which I guided him. He agreed. What transpired surprised both of us. During Mike's guided journey with me, all kinds of traumatic memories came out that he hadn't remembered in his self-guided trips. Fortunately, I could gently lead him through these memories in a profoundly healing way. Yet, Mike and I wondered why these memories hadn't surfaced in previous non-guided journeys. It was as if the safety and skills I could provide allowed Mike's previously hidden material to surface and be healed. I've heard similar stories from many people I've trained. Somehow, a person's subconscious seems to know when to surface challenging material, and a good guide can definitely make that more likely.

Assuming you're an individual planning to use a guide, I suggest you try a one-hour Zoom "discovery call" session with whomever you're considering attending to you. If you feel that your one-hour session went well, you can confidently book a time for your entire MDMA journey. If you feel uncomfortable with your potential guide, I suggest you hold off. When clients contact me, I always recommend a one-hour Zoom "discovery call" to see if we're a good match. If we are, we book a five-hour journey. If not, I refer them to someone I think will better suit their needs.

Last, but not least, it's important to know that people react to MDMA in various ways. While I've never dealt with a full-on "freak-out," I've known other therapists who have reported such things. Fortunately, it is very, very rare. That's why I feel safe enough to do sessions over Zoom. Yet, as previously mentioned, I always ask my clients to have a friend or mate somewhere in the general vicinity in case they feel a need for company. Most of the time, a person who feels anxious on MDMA can be easily calmed down by verbal reassurance and suggesting they take some slow, deep breaths. Alternatively, having a person shake their body or take a shower can be very calming. If those suggestions don't work, a guide can always call the nearby friend or mate whose phone number they previously requested—to be with the person having a hard time.

Unpleasant Side Effects

I should note that many people who take MDMA go through a 10 to 20-minute "discombobulation" period when they first come on to the drug. During this short period of time, they can feel quite uncomfortable. It's as if their mind has let go of a trapeze they've been holding onto, and yet they haven't fully grasped the next trapeze—so they feel ungrounded. When clients are going through this phase, I reassure them that it will quickly pass and that they'll soon enter a more peaceful and comfortable experience. My reassurance is usually all they need to relax with the new sensations and slight nausea they may be experiencing.

For perhaps 5% of folks who take MDMA, they feel *very* anxious when they first come onto the drug. In such cases, I guide them in a short meditation where I have them focus on their breath or the sensations of their feet. If that doesn't help much, I ask them questions to bring up a more positive mindset. Questions that I've found helpful include:

What is something or someone you're grateful for in your life?

What part of your body currently feels the most relaxed or comfortable?

What have you done in the last year that was fun or made you feel good?

On extremely rare occasions, a person taking MDMA may feel increased fear for more than 30 minutes, and their body will begin shaking, trembling, or even vomiting. When this happens, I let them know that shaking is a helpful way to release the fear that has been "stored" in their body. I often encourage them to stand up and allow the shaking or trembling to continue. After a short while, their fear and shaking will usually dissipate, leading to a calmer and more relaxed state of mind and body. If a client feels they may vomit, I encourage them to get a bowl in case they feel the need to do so. While vomiting on MDMA is rare, in most cases it quickly leads to a client feeling much better.

Two more unpleasant side effects can accompany an MDMA journey. The first is the tendency for a person's jaw to tighten during their session. Luckily, this tendency can be significantly diminished or eliminated if a person takes 300 to 400 mg of Magnesium Glycinate with their MDMA medicine. Such supplements are inexpensive and available at Amazon.com or any health food store. Taking another 200 to 300 mg of Magnesium Glycinate at bedtime after a session can also be an excellent way to relax and help a person fall asleep.

Other unpleasant side effects can happen a day or two after an MDMA session. For about half of folks who take MDMA, the day after their session will be accompanied by some slight tiredness and/or sadness. These feelings can be partly due to the emotional content of the therapy, and partly due to having just dumped a lot of serotonin into their brain. I tell my clients that, if possible, try to take it easy the day after their session in case they feel tired. Having a day to rest and reflect can be an essential part of the MDMA healing experience. However, for perhaps 5% of folks who take MDMA, the experience can result in considerable tiredness and/or sadness for up to three days following their session. While rare, if this happens to you or a client, know that such effects will soon dissipate. To make unpleasant aftereffects even less likely, it helps to know of certain supplements and practices that help with a swift recovery.

It is important to note that scientific research on the following recommendations is limited. Instead, these recommendations are based on the opinions of many people who have an extensive history of MDMA use. Yet, because everyone's body is unique, what works for one person may not work for another. Therefore, if you are the type of person who historically has had a hard time the day after a journey, I'd recommend trying whatever feels right to you in the suggestions below. The more things you try, the more likely you'll find something that works well for you. So, without further delay, here are my top 8 recommendations to lessen any unpleasant aftereffects of taking MDMA:

1. During your journey, drink plenty of water—especially water that has electrolytes in it. A popular brand called "Smartwater" has electrolytes added to their purified water. Another option is to drink coconut water—which naturally has electrolytes in it.

2. Take a 100 mg 5-HTP supplement and a 300 mg Magnesium Glycinate supplement before bed the night of your MDMA journey. The morning after your journey, take both supplements again with a nutritious breakfast.

3. Avoid alcohol the day of and the day after your journey. If you feel a headache the night of your journey or the day after, it's okay to take Ibuprofen (Advil).

4. Many people say supplements such as Vitamin C, CoQ10, and grape seed extract help them recover from an MDMA session. You can take these the day before, the day of, and the day after your journey.

5. Nutritious food and green drinks are always helpful for your body, especially after an MDMA session. If you're sensitive, take such things before and after your journey.

6. Gentle exercise, baths, or a dry or steam sauna can also aid in recovery.

7. If you have difficulty falling asleep the night of your journey, taking any standard sleep medication is fine.

8. If you have a very sensitive body, or have had difficulty the day after MDMA in the past, one more additional supplement can help: Try taking what's called ALA + ALC. You can buy it inexpensively online at sites such as this: https://www.vitacost.com/vitacost-alpha-lipoic-acid-acetyl-l-carnitine-hcl-60-capsules

   Take one capsule when starting and ending your journey, two before bed, then three capsules the next day.

Listen to your body and try to intuit what would make it feel good. If you feel tired the day after a journey, you may simply need to nap or rest more than usual. Some initial studies have found that a person's expectations about how they'll feel after a journey are probably the biggest factor affecting their feelings. If you think you'll feel tired, you probably will be. If not, you'll likely feel normal.

Legal Concerns:

It is essential to be aware of the legal status of MDMA in your jurisdiction. As of late 2023, it is still illegal in almost every country–Australia being a notable exception. Each country has its own laws and penalties for MDMA possession, and it's best to do a Google search to ascertain how steep the consequences are in the country you live in. In some countries in Africa or East Asia, you could face many years of imprisonment for possession of MDMA. Each person must decide what level of risk they're willing to take based on the information they gather for their particular country.

Now that I've discussed all the contraindications and concerns when taking MDMA, you may feel hesitant—or even paranoid about trying

it. However, I should point out that most problems I've mentioned are very rare. In addition, the challenges associated with taking MDMA can usually be mitigated with the right supplements, care, and information. The fact is that a list of precautions usually accompanies any powerful medicine. That's why when you see a new medication advertised, an announcer inevitably states something like, "In rare cases, this medicine can lead to nausea, headache, diarrhea, and vomiting." Yikes! Fortunately, MDMA is extremely safe when taken in an appropriate dose while in a safe setting, so my advice is to simply avoid doing anything stupid.

I've thrown a lot of helpful information at you in this chapter. Before trying MDMA-assisted therapy, I want you to know all the good and bad information so you can make the best decision for you. So, take the precautions listed as simply prudent advice meant to avoid rare cases of difficulty. In truth, for the vast majority of users, taking MDMA is safe, fun, enlightening, and a fantastic learning experience.

CHAPTER 3

A BRIEF HISTORY OF MDMA

"Penalties against possession of a drug should not be more damaging to an individual than the use of the drug itself."

— Jimmy Carter, Former President of the USA

Although this book is written to be very practical, I thought a chapter devoted to the history of MDMA would help provide an entertaining context for how it's thought of today. The story is entertaining because an entire cast of characters, ranging from saintly to sinister, have played a role in the MDMA story. Each person encountering MDMA places different hopes, fears, and reactions to its powerful effect. Since every era and person differs, you could say MDMA has been through several different "trips." Seeing how this molecule has been viewed in so many different ways shows how central mental set and setting are to the effects it creates.

...So, once upon a time, the German pharmaceutical company, Merck serendipitously discovered MDMA in 1912. However, its psychoactive properties remained largely unnoticed for several decades. MDMA was initially developed to be a potential appetite suppressant and vasoconstrictor. However, due to a lack of significant medical applications, further research on MDMA was not pursued. The compound remained in obscurity until the mid-1970s, when it resurfaced and gained attention for its remarkable effects on human consciousness.

It was during the 1970s that the influential American chemist Alexander "Sasha" Shulgin rediscovered MDMA. Fascinated by its psychoactive properties, Shulgin became an advocate for its potential therapeutic applications. He conducted extensive experiments on himself and others, documenting the subjective effects and advocating for its therapeutic potential.

Shulgin collaborated with therapists, introducing them to MDMA and promoting its use in therapeutic settings. He believed that the compound had unique qualities that could facilitate emotional introspection, empathy, and communication, making it a valuable tool for psychotherapy. Shulgin's efforts helped popularize MDMA as a therapeutic aid and contributed to its growing reputation.

Soon, the therapeutic use of MDMA expanded beyond individual therapy to include couples counseling and trauma treatment. While MDMA was gaining recognition for its therapeutic potential, it gradually made its way into the nightclub and party scene. In the early 1980s, it became associated with the emerging "rave culture" and all-night dance parties—especially in Texas of all places. At a place called The Stark Club, gays, rednecks, Mexicans and Americans all danced together on Ecstasy as one happy family. People who consumed MDMA reported increased sociability and an overall positive mood, making it appealing for recreational use in the energetic club environment.

I encountered MDMA at the college I attended, UC Santa Barbara, in 1979. I had become familiar with LSD and figured this "new drug" would take me on a similar trip. I was pleasantly surprised to find it was a completely different experience. As an emotionally repressed and nerdy kid, I was neither empathic nor in touch with my feelings. For me, MDMA was a ticket to a whole new world. When my girlfriend and

I took it together, I learned what intimacy, honesty, and empathy were all about for perhaps the first time. Like a religious zealot, I thought everyone should take this drug and discover the authentic experience of love. It took many years for me to understand that any drug experience, including MDMA, is primarily determined by a person's background, set, and setting.

How the drug became illegal is an interesting story. Like me, many therapists and psychiatrists at the time saw that this molecule was the best thing to happen to psychology since Sigmund Freud. But sensational media coverage only spoke of its recreational drug use and spouted its many supposed risks. Never mind that the risks were not based on actual science. However, based on the testimony of many psychiatrists, the DEA's Law Judge, Francis Young, recommended keeping MDMA legally available for research purposes. However, John Lawn, the administrator for the DEA at the time, was not a fan of Ecstasy—either as a drug or as an emotion. So, despite the overwhelming evidence presented by many psychiatrists–and the DEA's judge's ruling–John Lawn overruled Judge Young and classified MDMA as illegal, even for research purposes. That was in October of 1986, and the law hasn't changed since then.

Next, as law enforcement efforts intensified, illicit manufacturers sought to circumvent legal restrictions by producing and marketing alternative substances marketed as Ecstasy. These substances often contained various chemicals and compounds, some much more dangerous than MDMA. The widespread use of these contaminated pills led to a rise in adverse effects and contributed to the negative reputation associated with Ecstasy. Media coverage further stigmatized MDMA, emphasizing its potential dangers while downplaying its prospective therapeutic benefits. MDMA became associated with reckless behavior, party culture, and illicit drug use, overshadowing its earlier promising applications in therapy.

Despite the legal troubles and negative publicity, the desire to explore MDMA's therapeutic potential persisted among researchers, therapists, and advocates. In the 1980s, Rick Doblin was an enthusiastic proponent of MDMA. Doblin's interest in psychedelics began in his youth when he had personal experiences with these substances. He later pursued a doctorate in Public Policy from Harvard University. At Harvard, Doblin wrote his dissertation on the regulation of the medical uses of psychedelics and marijuana. This research formed the foundation of his lifelong commitment to studying the therapeutic potential of these substances.

MAPS and Studies Begin

In 1986, Doblin founded MAPS, which stands for Multidisciplinary Association for Psychedelic Studies. Its primary goal was to research the safety and efficacy of psychedelic drugs for therapeutic purposes. MAPS initially faced significant challenges due to the stigma associated with psychedelics because of their prohibition in the 1970s. However, Doblin was not to be deterred. Through MAPS, Doblin began advocating for the therapeutic use of MDMA. Over 35 years, MAPS has played a crucial role in raising money for research, supporting clinical trials, and lobbying for regulatory changes. Along the way, MAPS and Rick Doblin have faced immense obstacles to doing any research with MDMA. Even when research was finally allowed on squirrel monkeys and baboons, scientists seemingly tried to sabotage the studies.

George Ricaurte, a neurologist at John Hopkins, was hired by Doblin to research the potential toxicity effects of MDMA. Doblin hoped that hiring a respected scientist and having his findings show MDMA was safe would help lead to human clinical trials. Yet, Doblin was unaware at the time that Ricaurte would soon become known for using government grants to find everything possible that might be dangerous about MDMA. Ricaurte would later proclaim—with zero evidence—that "even one dose of MDMA can lead to permanent brain damage." Doblin had initially felt that Ricaurte was an impartial scientist, but as he later reflected, he said, "Over time, I saw that was not the case."

The U.S. government often lavishly funded labs like Ricaurte's to try to prove the harm drugs did to people. The media often used their research to create headlines such as "Proof that Ecstasy Damages the Brain." Ricaurte's lab got paid well for promoting highly misleading and non-scientific statements about MDMA's harmful effects. One anti-drug campaign funded by the National Institute on Drug Abuse proclaimed, "Ecstasy causes holes in the brain." The "holes" were, in truth, just depictions of areas of the brain with lesser blood flow, but such fine points were missed by Oprah, MTV, and other media. In response to such scary proclamations, in the year 2000, U.S. lawmakers passed the Ecstasy Anti-Proliferation Act. This increased the sentencing for dealing MDMA as more punishable, dose per dose, than heroin.

In 2002, Ricaurte published a study in the prestigious journal *Science*. The article claimed that when his staff injected ten squirrel monkeys and baboons with a dose of MDMA, two of them died, and two others collapsed from heatstroke. Even though the findings seemed suspicious, *Science* published the results, possibly because the journal received pressure from the U.S. government. Of course, the study was widely reported in the news. But months later, *Science* issued a rare and startling retraction. It was learned that Ricaurte hadn't given the animals MDMA, but had dosed them with a large amount of methamphetamine–often known as crystal meth. Furthermore, Ricaurte and his colleagues never provided a satisfactory explanation for how this "mix-up" happened.

Credible research since this scandal has shown evidence that when MDMA is given in large, repeated doses to lab animals, temporary damage to the serotonin system results. However, evidence also indicates that when lab animals stop being given large quantities of MDMA, the serotonin system soon repairs itself. Between the *Science* retraction and the ongoing neurotoxicity studies with MDMA showing very minor effects, the FDA became open to considering human clinical trials. Rick Doblin chose to focus on using MDMA to help treatment-resistant PTSD. Since this was a big problem for veterans, and there were no good treatments for this condition, Doblin felt that this was an excellent place to start human trials.

As stated in Chapter 1, this MAPS-sponsored clinical trial proved to be an astonishing success, leading to FDA trials. The results from these studies played a crucial role in rekindling scientific interest in psychedelics for mental health treatment.

Psychedelics Go Mainstream

Meanwhile, around 1995 I began leading occasional journeys with MDMA in my office. I became aware of an entire "underground" industry of therapists and guides who helped people "trip" on LSD, MDMA, and psilocybin. I noticed that the effects of each of these drugs were often profound. However, when a client was on MDMA, I felt like I could do two years of therapy with them in an afternoon. I decided to specialize in MDMA therapy. Then, when the pandemic hit in 2020, I could no longer lead these journeys in my office. As an experiment, I decided to try a Zoom session with a client and was astonished at how well it worked. This client told her friends about how it changed her life, and soon I was inundated with clients wanting to do this therapy over Zoom. As word spread that MDMA would eventually be made into a legal medically prescribed drug, people asked me if I'd teach a course on how to guide people effectively. The rest, as they say, is history—and this book.

In the 2010s, the idea that trauma affects our lives began to enter mainstream culture. In 2014, Bessel van der Kolk's book, *The Body Keeps the Score*, introduced millions of folks to the effects of trauma on physical and mental health. Then, in 2018 respected science writer Michael Pollan wrote a bestselling book about psychedelics titled *How to Change*

Your Mind. This book eventually led to a Netflix documentary by the same name. The book, Netflix show, and research results all contributed to a gradual sea change in how the media viewed psychedelics. As Covid hit and mental health took a nosedive worldwide, interest in alternative approaches to mental health skyrocketed. Respected sources such as *The New York Times* began regularly writing front-page articles touting the extraordinary healing properties of MDMA and other psychedelics.

Currently, many ongoing studies investigate MDMA's potential in treating other mental health conditions, such as anxiety, depression, and addiction. Preliminary findings suggest that MDMA may have a broad range of therapeutic applications beyond PTSD. Researchers are also examining the mechanisms of action underlying MDMA's therapeutic effects. Recently, scientists have become interested in how MDMA (and other psychedelics) increase people's ability to learn new behavior—what's called the "critical learning period." MDMA's ability to increase empathy and enhance emotional introspection has been attributed to its effects on neurotransmitters, especially serotonin and oxytocin. Understanding these mechanisms may contribute to the development of targeted and potentially even more effective treatments.

The future of MDMA in therapy holds immense potential. As research continues, there is growing optimism that MDMA-assisted therapy will become a recognized and regulated treatment option for various mental health conditions. When I interviewed Rick Doblin of MAPS in July of 2023, I asked him how he thought the future of MDMA would unfold. Of course, he could only speculate on who would be allowed to prescribe MDMA. Rick suggested, "I do not think it should be limited to psychiatrists…the likelihood is that doctors of any kind will, but they may need a small training program. It could be a couple of hours." Then, I asked Rick about who will be certified to be a guide for journeys. He replied, "We (MAPS) don't want to be the only provider of the training, but we want it ideally to be provided by us or by groups that we authorize." How things eventually unfold will be determined by the FDA when they finally make MDMA a legal medicine.

Rick Doblin's contributions to the field of psychedelic research and advocacy cannot be overstated. Through his work with MAPS, he has played a crucial role in re-establishing psychedelic research and has helped pave the way for the integration of psychedelics into mainstream medicine and mental health care. As I've gotten to know Rick, I can also say he's a very fun, open, and great guy. His dogged persistence and powerful sense of mission over 40 years have inspired thousands of people. In July of 2023, MAPS held the largest psychedelic conference in history. Over 13,000 people attended a five-day conference in Denver, Colorado, with over 300 speakers. As Bob Dylan once sang, "The times they are a-changing."

Rick and his MAPS cohorts have also supported research on psilocybin, LSD, Ayahuasca, marijuana, and ibogaine. In addition, Rick recently asked me to be involved in a study to ascertain the effects of MDMA in couples' therapy. I am currently working with other folks to document the effects of MDMA in helping couples experience more harmony. Over the years, Doblin's work has garnered support from many public figures, politicians, and law enforcement officials who recognize the benefits of psychedelic-assisted therapies. While the history of Rick Doblin is ongoing and may have developed further since this writing, his efforts show the power of what one committed person can do to make a positive impact on the world.

CHAPTER 4

SET, SETTING, AND RITUAL

"MDMA is a gateway drug! It swings open the gate to tactile, emotional, and spiritual exploration and opens the door to the heart."

— Alan Aldous, author

Most people who have taken a psychedelic drug have heard that creating a helpful set and setting are key to enjoying a beneficial experience. For those less familiar with psychedelics, "set" refers to one's mental state before taking a drug, and "setting" refers to the environment in which one takes a psychedelic. Since psychedelics–including MDMA–often amplify what's already happening in one's head and environment, you want to ensure things are all good before you launch. Therefore, you should avoid taking MDMA after receiving bad news, or taking any psychedelic in a place where you feel unsafe or uncomfortable.

Tom, an engineer in his thirties, emailed me about guiding him on an MDMA journey. As we talked over Zoom, he told me that he had never tried it before. When I asked him why he wanted to give it a try, he said he'd heard it induces a state of love and deep inner peace. After our call, Tom contacted my connection, who mailed him the medicine and supplements to reduce potential unpleasant side effects. When I saw Tom again on the day of his journey, I could tell he was thrilled to finally be diving into a long-awaited experience.

Over the course of almost five hours, I guided Tom into many wonderful internal places. Since he wanted to open to more joy and love, that's how we spent the bulk of our session time together. It was deeply gratifying to see him melting into what he described as "more love than I've ever felt before." Since the session went so well, I was surprised to find an alarming email from him the following day. Tom's email said, "You tricked me. That was very strange. I didn't sleep last night. Call me as soon as you can." I immediately called Tom and asked him what happened after our session.

Tom began the conversation, "So...I didn't expect that. You tricked me."

I replied, "I don't know what you're referring to."

Tom said, "After our session, I took what was supposed to be the magnesium supplement your friend had sent me to help me relax that night. However, after about 40 minutes, I realized that what I thought was magnesium was the actual MDMA pill! I began tripping heavily and feeling a lot of love. Then I realized that meant the trip you had guided me on wasn't actual MDMA–I had been high on a magnesium supplement! You tricked me."

I was amazed–and a bit amused–at what Tom was telling me. I assured Tom that I didn't mean to trick him and that my friend who had sent the pills evidently failed to clearly mark which pills were which. Then I told Tom that his initial venture into love and joy (while on a magnesium supplement) meant he had the power to tap into such feelings without any chemical help. When I told Tom that, his attitude suddenly shifted. Now he saw the whole "mishap" as a great lesson for realizing joy and love were always hidden within himself. In fact, he reported that the actual MDMA pill (which he took later that evening) felt very similar to what he had experienced earlier with me. ...Such is the power of the placebo effect and the power of creating a proper set and setting for taking MDMA medicine.

Setting Things Up

As my experience with Tom indicates, creating positive expectations for a journey, and the skillful help of a guide, are key aspects of what makes MDMA-assisted therapy so effective. To ensure my clients have a good experience, I do an initial Zoom call to create the best possible set and setting. During this one-hour session, I like to cover many topics. First, I want to make sure my client is comfortable with me and my approach. In rare cases, I realize a potential client is not a good match for this medicine, or that contraindications interfere with their receiving value. As mentioned in Chapter 2, the most common things I look for are if a person is currently on SSRI anti-depressant medications or on MAOI medication.

Once I've established rapport with a client and I recognize they're a good candidate for a journey, we dive into their reason for taking MDMA. People reach out to me for various reasons, but the most common motives include helping them overcome challenges such as trauma, depression, anxiety, or an issue in their relationship. In addition, lately, I've had many people come to me hoping to create more joy and love in their life. Helping people clarify what they hope to achieve from a session is a key factor in creating a positive outcome.

It's easier to hit a target if you know what you're aiming for. I learned this lesson in college when my roommate, Tony, challenged me to a one-on-one basketball game. Tony was on the varsity basketball team, so such a game would likely be a slaughter. Yet, I told Tony, "I'll play you a one-on-one game as long as I get to bring a one-ounce gadget and place it anywhere on the court." Somewhat perplexed, Tony agreed to my terms. At the court, I took out my one-ounce "gadget," a blindfold, and strategically placed it over Tony's eyes. Then I announced, "Let the game begin." Admittedly, it was still somewhat close! Yet, I managed to beat one of the best basketball players in Los Angeles because I knew where to aim my efforts, and Tony did not. This lesson taught me that the more precisely you can define someone's target, the better the chance of helping them achieve what they want.

Most people only have a vague idea of what they hope to achieve during their session. To clarify a person's intention, I often ask them questions to help them be more specific. Common questions I might ask at this point include:

1. What motivated you to seek a journey at this time?
2. What's your history with MDMA or other psychedelics, and why have you taken them?
3. What concerns–if any–do you have?
4. What do you hope to experience through this work?
5. What does a successful journey look like to you?
6. What spiritual beliefs or practices are important to you, and how might this medicine align with those beliefs?
7. What are the top three issues you'd potentially like to explore while on this medicine?
8. Why did you choose each of those issues?
9. What do you believe is keeping you from your goals at this point in your life?
10. If you had a magic wand, what are one or two things you wish you could change about yourself?

Once I know what a client wants to achieve from a session, I will relay some basic information about how such sessions work. I go over things like cost, confidentiality, ethics, and boundaries. I state that, even if we do a session in person (which is rare nowadays), I cannot touch them other than to hold their hand. By stating clear physical boundaries, I aim to help the client feel as safe as possible during their session. Next, we talk about their past experiences with psychedelics and the importance of creating a private and cozy environment to take this medicine. I often suggest they make a playlist of music they might want to listen to during their journey. Finally, I request they make sure that all potential distractions (kids, dogs, mates, etc.) are handled beforehand and that they set aside five hours for their journey.

Whether you're taking MDMA alone, guiding a friend or client, or with a group of people, an important consideration is how much of the medicine to take and the purity of what you're taking. The purity of the drug matters...and so does dosage. Let's first talk about the purity of the medicine. While Europe faces a flood of high-potency Ecstasy pills, the US has the opposite problem: pills or powders sold as "Ecstasy" or "Molly" often contain very little or no MDMA. According to a range of sources, anywhere between 30% and 60% of what is being sold as Molly or Ecstasy in the USA is not pure MDMA. Much of what is sold in the US as MDMA is actually mixed with bath salts, methamphetamine, or other mind-altering compounds.

As I mentioned in Chapter 2, before ingesting what you think is MDMA, have it tested—or at least know that the batch you're getting is from a trusted source. According to an article published in the respected PubMed online resource, the difficult hangovers that often accompany an MDMA journey are almost always the result of the impurity of the medicine taken and/or the detrimental environment in which it is ingested. People who take pure MDMA in a suitable environment tend to feel fine the day after their journey—especially if they take commonly recommended supplements afterward.

You also want to be smart about how much MDMA you or a person you're guiding is taking. A typical dose of MDMA tends to be about 125mg. If you take under 70mg, you might not feel it; if you take over

200 mg, you may feel overstimulated or nauseous. When I work with clients, I suggest they procure a 125mg pill or capsule and a 60 mg "booster" if they want more MDMA 90 minutes into their journey. I've found that about half of my clients decide to take the booster, and half don't. Just as a little bit of alcohol can be fun, and a lot can make you sick, MDMA does different things at different dosage levels. In addition, some people are more sensitive to MDMA than others—just as people have different tolerances for alcohol. By starting with a typical dose and having a booster ready in case you need more, you maximize your chances of having a good trip.

The Power of Ritual

For many centuries, people's lives were infused with various rituals. Nowadays, elaborate rituals involving substances are much rarer than they used to be. That is unfortunate because when rituals are done well, they pave the way for transformation. Fortunately, creating a great mental set and setting can be like preparing for a pilgrimage. If done mindfully, each part of the MDMA preparation process can add to the sense that something important is about to take place. The search for a guide, getting good medicine, taking preparatory supplements, and clearing one's schedule can all be like steps in one's pilgrimage. By the time the medicine is finally ingested, the prior steps all help to create a mental set conducive to a great outcome.

There are many ways to enhance the sense of ritual inherent in an MDMA journey. I like to explore what a client has used in the past to bring added meaning and intention to events in their life. When a person includes meaningful rituals in their journey, it tends to increase the depth of insight and transformative effect of the medicine. If a person has had good psychedelic encounters in the past, asking about their experiences can help infuse greater meaning into the journey they're about to take. Once again, creating a good mental "set" inevitably leads to a great experience.

Many years ago, I led a spiritual group of 30 students who would watch movies that conveyed a powerful message. After watching a movie, I'd have them write down what they learned from viewing the profound movie I had presented. At one point, I was going to be away, so I gave what I thought was the movie *Gandhi* to a friend to play for this group of people. Little did I know, but the actual movie in the DVD sleeve was the movie *Men in Black 2*.

In case you haven't seen it, *Men in Black 2* was blasted by critics and audiences alike for being stupid and boring. However, this group was conditioned to see the "profound message" within any movie I presented to them. Evidently, their past experience and intention to see something profound in *Men in Black 2* overwhelmed the inanity of the actual film. Virtually everyone wrote glowing reviews of what they had learned from this movie. One participant even reported, "*Men in Black 2's* message has dramatically impacted how I see the world in a positive way. It was transformative."

I tell you this funny story because it shows how positive expectations, along with a clear intention, can be so powerful in how we view or experience something. Therefore, make sure all MDMA journeys you're part of involve some ritual. Previously, I mentioned that when I work with someone, I ask them to create a playlist of songs–that are primarily without lyrics–that they might want to hear on their journey. In fact, only about 10% of my clients decide to listen to any of their playlists while on the medicine. Nevertheless, I think the simple act of creating a playlist helps my clients prepare for their journey. On the other hand, in the MAPS protocol, the *therapists* create a playlist for their clients. I think this is a missed opportunity. After all, a client's music is likely to be much more meaningful to them than the music a therapist picks.

Another way to add ritual to an MDMA session is to use a person's spiritual beliefs and tendencies as a prelude to a journey. Most folks have some form of habitual way to denote a special occasion. This could include saying a particular prayer, invoking a spiritual being, holding a special object, or perhaps reading from a Holy book. Sometimes I suggest that a client come up with their own unique way of preparing for their journey. Below is a list of things my clients have used to help them emotionally and spiritually prepare for their journey work:

1. Taking a bath, shower, or ritually washing their hands before ingesting their medicine.

2. Listening to a favorite song as they "come on" to the MDMA.

3. Looking at photos of people and animals they love before their trip.

4. Reading a favorite poem or passage from a book that has deep meaning for them.

5. Holding an object that is special to them, such as a gift from a friend, a favorite crystal, or an object from a deceased loved one.

6. Doing a particular type of meditation that helps with centering.

7. Fasting or eating only certain kinds of food the day of and the day before a journey.

It can be fun to come up with a unique ritual that feels just right. In most cases, people have something that they've used in the past that helps evoke a special feeling. They simply need to be reminded about it and encouraged to use it.

When I meet someone (usually on Zoom) the day of the journey, I often ask them if they have done any particular ritual before ingesting the drug. If they have not, I suggest they do a very simple one with me that has to do with giving thanks to various people and things in their life. Focusing on gratitude is a great and easy way to create a beneficial mental set. Yet, before we do this exercise together, I share with them a little story about a "magical mantra" I received from a guru in India for helping me feel deep gratitude.

Many years ago, a friend named Fred returned from India looking incredibly happy. So I asked him, "What changed for you in India?" He mentioned that his guru had given him a magical mantra for feeling overwhelming gratitude. Of course, I asked him what this mantra was, but Fred told me I'd have to go to India to get it directly from his guru.

Well, I knew the importance of gratitude, so I flew all the way to India to ask this guru about his amazing mantra. After a couple of days of flying, taking rickshaws, and waiting to see the guru, I finally got to talk to this man in a flowing white robe. When I asked him about his mantra for helping people feel gratitude, the holy man said, "Ah yes, my mantra is the most powerful mantra on Earth!" He leaned in to whisper it to me. I was very excited. He said, "Whenever possible, repeat the following words. The mantra I give you is the words…thank you."

I figured the holy man was joking, but he seemed totally serious when I looked at him. I couldn't believe I had traveled all that way for such a stupid, simple mantra. I looked at the guru and practically shouted, "Thank you!? That's it?!"

The guru said, "No, 'That's it' is the mantra you *have* been using, and that makes you feel like you never have enough. My mantra is 'thank you,' not 'that's it'. Thinking 'that's it' will take you nowhere!"

I was pissed off, so I gave the guru a sneer and, in my most sarcastic voice possible, said, "Well, thank you for nothing!"

The guru smiled and said, "You must say it from your heart many times a day— so when you eat good food, say, 'thank you' from your heart. When you see your child, a sunset, or your pet, say 'thank you' from your heart, and soon you will be filled with overwhelming gratitude."

I was still pissed off and highly disappointed, but I figured I'd try it since I had traveled all that way. As I left the ashram, I got a taxi, and to my delight, it had air-conditioning that actually worked. In gratitude for this comfort, I felt into my heart and said, "Thank you" to the Universe. Then, I got to my hotel room. In my bathroom was a bottle of purified drinking water. As I quickly drank it, I felt my heart again and said, "Thank you." Next, I opened my computer to Skype with my wife. As my laptop came to life, I said another "thank you" for this marvelous machine. Next, my wife appeared on the screen. At that point, it hit me how amazing this was. I was talking instantly to my wife from across the globe—for free! I felt incredible gratitude for Skype, my wife, for technology. Thank you, thank you, thank you. Tears started to flow down my face. My wife looked at me and said, "That must be a really magical mantra."

I replied, "You have no idea…"

After I share this story, I ask my client to think of someone or something in their life they are grateful for, then feel their heart before saying "thank you" to the Universe for this particular blessing. Then, I do the same for a blessing in my life. I suggest we go back and forth three more times, saying "thank you" for specific blessings in our lives. By the time this little gratitude practice is done, we both feel humble, present and in a good frame of mind.

Creating a beneficial set and setting is both an art form and a science. The art part involves listening to your heart, being creative, and enjoying the process. The science part consists in asking the right questions to help yourself or another get in touch with what is truly sacred. When you combine the medicine of MDMA with creating a beneficial set and setting, magic and miracles are the most likely result.

CHAPTER 5

MDMA VS. OTHER
PSYCHEDELIC THERAPY

"MDMA is a miraculous drug for psychotherapy. It allows people to go through therapy and process painful memories without feeling overwhelmed or traumatized."

— Rick Doblin, founder of MAPS

MDMA is only one of many drugs that have, in recent years, gained attention for their therapeutic potential. Various psychedelics are gaining mainstream popularity thanks to books such as Michael Pollan's "How to Change Your Mind," and publicized clinical trials. Whereas all psychedelics were once considered highly dangerous, now the pendulum is swinging in the opposite direction. Nowadays, I rarely go a month without seeing an article on the front page of the *New York Times* suggesting that psychedelics can cure everything that ails us in modern society. In this chapter, I'll briefly explain some of the key differences between a journey on MDMA and a journey on four other drugs: LSD, psilocybin, Ketamine, and 5-MeO-DMT. Once the similarities and differences are established, I'll describe what a typical MDMA therapy session is like hour by hour.

Each of the five drugs described in this chapter has its own distinctive therapeutic potential and experience. The fact that they are all so different is a feature, not a bug. Each of these drugs serves a unique purpose. After hearing more about LSD, psilocybin, Ketamine, and 5-MeO-DMT, you may be interested in pursuing more information online about their therapeutic potential. A good resource for learning more about these and other drugs is the website: www.Erowid.com

Psilocybin

High (pun intended) amongst the alternatives to MDMA therapy is psilocybin. Psilocybin is the psychoactive compound found in "magic mushrooms." Psilocybin interacts with serotonin receptors in the brain, leading to altered perception, introspection, and even mystical experiences. Psilocybin-assisted therapy has shown promising results in treating various mental health conditions, including depression, anxiety, and addiction.[3] Taken under favorable conditions, it can promote emotional breakthroughs and a sense of interconnectedness.

Psilocybin-assisted therapy has also shown promising results in clinical trials, and several studies are ongoing. Although still illegal in most of the world, in recent months, I've noticed it is easily bought over the web (such as at www.soulcybin.org), and it has been decriminalized and sold in stores in cities such as Denver, Colorado, and Oakland California. Therapy with psilocybin is often done in a one-shot session in which people take a large amount of the drug. A typical trip lasts from 4 to 6 hours. Through such experiences, it is hoped that participants will have life-altering–even mystical–experiences that help them see their life in new ways. Indeed, research suggests that the intense and hallucinogenic experiences brought on by this drug can be helpful for several conditions. Yet, many people also experience challenging trips, and this drug is best taken in a highly favorable setting with a trained guide.

[3] https://www.hopkinsmedicine.org/psychiatry/research/psychedelics-research.html

Recently, many people have used psilocybin in a manner called "microdosing." Microdosing involves taking a small amount of a drug rather frequently, and then going about a normal day. A typical microdose of psilocybin is about 1/10th of a standard dose, so that can be anywhere from 1/8th of a gram to 1/4th of a gram. A popular protocol for microdosing with mushrooms is to take a small dose every fourth day. This is called the Fadiman protocol, which basically involves skipping two days between doses. Many people and some research have shown that this protocol may be especially helpful for people in overcoming depression and feeling happier.[4]

For more information about various microdosing protocols and their potential benefits, you can go to www.microdosinginstitute.com

LSD

LSD-assisted therapy employs lysergic acid diethylamide. It was the drug Timothy Leary got kicked out of Harvard for promoting in the early 1960s. Starting in 1965, LSD was made illegal and classified as a dangerous drug with no therapeutic potential. However, before it was made illegal, studies suggested that it helped treat addiction, anxiety, and end-of-life distress.[5] Unfortunately, research was virtually ended when it was made illegal, and only in recent years have a few studies begun to explore its full therapeutic potential.

The subjective effects of LSD can vary widely, and the therapy aims to guide individuals through challenging and transformative experiences. During the 1960s and beyond, LSD was instrumental in turning millions of people on to new ideas and understandings. I was one of those people. My first LSD trip at age 16 was the greatest moment of my life up till that time. It showed me that the world was potentially different and more fun than I had imagined. During that trip, I decided to

---

[4] https://www.nytimes.com/2022/02/28/well/mind/microdosing-psychedelics.html
[5] https://www.frontiersin.org/articles/10.3389/fpsyt.2019.00943/full

dedicate my life to finding my way back to the joy, wonder, and fun I had experienced while on LSD. Within a week, I began meditating daily and reading books about consciousness and inner peace. I can clearly state that LSD changed the course of my life. At the same time, I can say it can be dangerous if not taken under favorable conditions. Since a typical "trip" lasts 9 to 12 hours, you want to ensure you have a trusted friend or guide nearby in case you need support.

While there are many similarities between LSD and psilocybin, there are also some key differences. These two drugs can often feel very much alike, and at medium to high dosages, they both can lead to interesting hallucinations. Yet, the much shorter duration of psilocybin makes it easier to use in a therapeutic context. In addition, many people report that LSD can often feel more "heady," whereas psilocybin can often feel more body-oriented. Even though their effects can be described as comparable, people who have tried both often report a distinct preference for one of them over the other.

Ketamine

Ketamine is a dissociative anesthetic drug used in medicine to induce and maintain anesthesia. In recent years, many studies have been done with Ketamine that indicates its value in helping people with treatment-resistant depression. It is also used as a pain management tool and a recreational drug. As an anti-depressant, the effect of a single dose soon wanes over time. Therefore, patients often receive repeated doses. A popular protocol for Ketamine therapy is to receive six doses over two weeks at a legally licensed Ketamine clinic. However, because Ketamine is a legally prescribed medicine, it's possible to do Ketamine therapy at home with the help of organizations such as Mindbloom.com and other online providers.

Besides being a popular medicine for treatment-resistant depression, Ketamine can also be helpful for the treatment of PTSD, suicidal ideation, and anxiety.[6] Unlike LSD or even MDMA, Ketamine doesn't last very long. Depending on whether it is administered through a nasal spray, IV, a shot, or snorted, it typically lasts between 15 and 90 minutes. In addition, its effects depend a lot on dosage. At tiny dosages, it has a pleasant, relaxing effect. At high dosages, it can lead to wild hallucinations and intensely positive or negative other-worldly experiences.

I have used Ketamine on several occasions and with a few clients. I have found that it can quickly help anxious people feel more relaxed and at peace. Clients with bodily discomfort find its analgesic effect to be especially pleasant. In my experience, I was impressed with how it helped me to meditate more deeply. Ketamine showed me that my mind always chooses certain thoughts and sensations to be more important than others. While under the influence of Ketamine, I could see that my worrying thoughts were no more important than how my feet felt. All sensations became wonderfully equal, and everything I felt seemed encased in a cocoon of soft tranquility. However, when I tried a higher dose of Ketamine, I just felt nauseous. With Ketamine, the long-term effects of repeated use are largely unknown and are an area of increasing investigation.

5-MeO-DMT

The drug 5-MeO-DMT is often referred to by its nicknames "bufo" or "toad" because it is secreted by the glands of the Colorado River toad. It is molecularly related to the drug DMT, but is quite different in its effect. Whereas DMT is very visual, 5-MeO-DMT is not, and is often considered to bring on a more intense and even more spiritual experience than DMT. In addition, DMT is found in the popular brew Ayahuasca, whereas 5-MeO-DMT is not. I first heard of this drug about twenty-five years ago. At the time, it was legal and not well-known.

---

[6] https://www.health.harvard.edu/blog/ketamine-for-treatment-resistant-depression-when-and-where-is-it-safe-202208092797

I had heard it was very intense and short-acting–between 10 and 30 minutes. Yet, nothing can really prepare you for what this drug does. At medium to high dosages (10 to 20 mg), as soon as you inhale the smoke, you're launched into a whole new world that is impossible to describe. It's like going from zero to 200 mph in three seconds.

If you're going to try this drug, make sure you start with a small dose (2 to 7 mg) so that you don't freak out. Although the drug can evoke fear due to its intensity and fast onset, there's nothing to really fear but fear itself. Physically, it's a relatively safe drug when smoked by itself. Yet, it should always be done with a "sitter" around because people sometimes thrash about in unpredictable ways when under its influence. Also, it's okay to combine this sacred medicine with marijuana, but it should not be combined with MDMA or MAO inhibitors due to contraindicated effects.

When people ask me, "What is a high dose 5-MeO-DMT trip like?" I give them a funny answer. I say, "If you believe in God, it will show you a glimpse of God. If you don't believe in God, you'll start to believe in God." I say this because the 80 or so folks I've introduced to this drug have consistently said such remarks. Virtually all my agnostic and atheist friends became believers in some kind of higher power after their experience with 5-MeO-DMT. That's pretty amazing. Of course, words fail to describe the experience. It is a unique and transformative experience that should not be taken lightly.

As with all drugs discussed in this chapter, your experience may vary. For the first time in history, a large portion of humanity is privy to many mind-altering substances. That's the good news. The bad news is that if you try enough different drugs, you'll probably find that some are clearly not for you. Only through careful and well-informed experimentation, hopefully with the help of a trusted guide, will you know which medicines are beneficial to you–and which are not. If you ever try any of these drugs and have a bad "trip," a group of volunteers called the Fireside Project can help you. They provide free emotional support during and after psychedelic experiences and are open from 11:00 am to 11:00 pm pst. They are located in the United States, and their number is 62-Fireside.

The descriptions offered here are just little glimpses of what some of the other options are for mind-altering therapies. Different strokes work for different folks. As mentioned, you can learn much more about each of these medicines at www.Erowid.com. However, if you want to dive deep into your psyche and work to overcome some challenges, I think MDMA is in a class by itself. Therefore, in the rest of this chapter, I will briefly describe the hour-by-hour structure of how I conduct a typical MDMA-assisted therapy session.

A Typical MDMA Therapy Session

As has already been discussed, MDMA can help individuals explore and process difficult emotions related to trauma, anxiety, and other mental health conditions. It typically lasts about 4 to 5 hours per "trip." It often takes 30 minutes to a full hour before a person notices its effects. When I work with people over Zoom, I usually suggest they take the medicine 20 to 30 minutes before we connect on Zoom. That way, they are close to feeling the drug when we connect on Zoom and start the therapeutic process.

Once I connect with someone on Zoom, I ask how they're doing and if they have any concerns about their upcoming trip. If someone expresses nervousness or anxiety, I assure them that such feelings are perfectly normal. Having spent an hour on Zoom (on a previous day) with each client beforehand, I sometimes know to use a special invocation, prayer, or song that they've requested to help set the stage for their sacred journey to begin. Many folks go through a "slightly uncomfortable" or anxious phase when they first feel the drug. It's as if they are leaving the "normal" world and have yet to fully enter the euphoric feelings of MDMA. If a client is experiencing anxiety, I assure them that this phase will soon pass.

As a client begins to feel the drug's effects, I like to ask them to describe what they notice. Having them describe their sensations and feelings does two things. First, it helps me to track their reaction, and if they are feeling anxious, to offer reassurance and suggestions for feeling more at ease. Second, describing a pleasant experience tends to deepen it. What you focus on grows. When clients describe feelings of euphoria, love, and peace, they soon fully embody such feelings. Since the sessions are audio recorded, many clients have found that listening to their own description of being high helps them tap into that experience when they're not on the drug. Halleluiah.

To better track a client's experience, I ask them to rate on a 1 to 10 scale what they are experiencing. I explain that a "10" means they are in high heaven, feeling great love, joy, and/or peace. A "1" means they feel incredibly anxious and uncomfortable, with a "5" denoting they feel average. Besides helping to understand their internal experience, the rating scale is also helpful in tracking how well different interventions work. For example, if a client says they're at an uncomfortable "2," I might guide them to a more comfortable experience. If they report they're now at a "7," I'll know that particular intervention was quite useful for them.

Once the MDMA is clearly being felt by the client, the true journey begins. At this point, I adhere to a rule known as "follow the medicine." What this means is that I let the client's current experience take precedence over any agenda or intention that they or I might have. Of course, since they've filled out an extensive client intake form and we've already spent an hour with each other on a previous Zoom call, I am already familiar with their issues and intentions. Yet, it often seems that the medicine has an intelligence all its own. They may have told me that they'd like to work on early childhood trauma, but to their surprise, the issue that arises is something totally different.

Many years ago, my wife and I were having trouble in our marriage. For about three months, she had been getting extremely angry at me for what seemed like very little things–such as forgetting to turn off the lights or failing to wash a dish. It was becoming intolerable for both of us. To find out why this newfound anger was surfacing, I hired a therapist to guide us through an MDMA couple's session. I figured we would learn what I was doing that had triggered my wife's anger. To everyone's surprise, a totally different issue surfaced.

It ends up that my wife's aunt had died three months earlier, and my wife had wanted to visit her before she died—but failed to do so due to being "too busy." Well, my wife felt incredibly guilty about this; unbeknownst to even her, she was very angry at herself. Her realization while on MDMA led to almost an hour of tears, and as she cried, I gently held her. Following this MDMA session, my wife's anger at me totally disappeared. I was amazed that neither she nor I knew what was really causing her upset. Yet, somehow, the medicine brought up the issue that was causing the real problem. Time after time, I've seen that MDMA seems to know what needs to be dealt with–even more than what I or my client might believe.

An easy way to let the medicine lead is to ask, when appropriate, "What are you noticing now?" That's it. As things arise, they become evident to the client. When they start talking (or emoting) about a particular issue or memory, that's where we turn our attention. In Part II of this book, I'll go into detail (including actual transcripts) about some of my therapeutic interventions when handling things like PTSD, anxiety, and depression. However, if I ask, "What are you noticing now?" and nothing interesting arises, that's when I look at my notes about their issues and challenges. From my notes, I choose something that seems like it would be beneficial to bring up, and we proceed from there.

One question I like to ask clients who are feeling especially good is, "What's normally in the way of feeling like this?" That always sparks an interesting conversation. Over time, I've developed a repertoire of many questions that clients have found useful to explore. A list of 20 of my more common questions can be found below–presented in no particular order. If you are guiding someone, you may find these questions very helpful to ask at an appropriate time. Generally, it's best to follow your curiosity in the moment, but these questions can serve as a good launching pad for exploration when you don't know what to do next.

20 Useful Questions:

1. Where do you see yourself at this point in your life?
2. What do you really want?
3. If you had no fear, how would you be different?
4. What do you feel is holding you back?
5. Why do you feel that is holding you back?
6. In your relationship with (fill in the blank), what do you want now?
7. What does this relationship need now to move forward?
8. What would you want to say to the person who did (fill in the blank) to you?
9. What do you feel you need to better heal this wound?
10. What's the payoff for you continuing to.......?
11. When you think of this changing, what comes up for you?
12. Who do you need or want to become to move forward in your life?
13. What do you need to let go of in your life right now?
14. What negative emotion do you tend to get stuck in or avoid the most?
15. What's the hardest thing for you to accept about yourself?
16. What keeps you from accepting that part of yourself?
17. What's your relationship to your deepest or divine self?
18. How do you tend to deal with uncomfortable emotions?

19. What might be a better way to handle difficult emotions?
20. What is this (relationship, situation, etc) teaching you?

In later chapters, I'll go into some depth as to how I use specific questions and modalities for various issues. Around four hours into our session, as the client gradually comes down from the medicine, I gently wind down the session. I may begin the "winding down" process by first asking if there is anything they feel an urgent need to talk about that we haven't already covered. Once that's resolved, I may ask a rather general question such as, "How has this been for you?" A question such as that invites a reflection about their entire experience and helps to bring things to a close. Finally, we discuss the importance of taking it easy the next day. I often suggest they spend time journaling, doing light exercise, and taking various supplements that may help them recover more quickly from any tiredness.

I always end my sessions by finding a time to schedule an integration session—generally about a week after their journey. The integration session is just as important as the actual multi-hour journey. In the integration session, I help people take the key insights they gained during their session and translate them into new behaviors to do in their day-to-day life. I request that my clients listen to the entire audio recording of their journey before we conduct our integration session. In Part III of this book, I describe in detail my protocol and methods for an integration session.

While the format I have presented here as a typical MDMA session is rather consistent, there is also room for plenty of spontaneity. Few sessions are entirely predictable, and my job is to follow the medicine and my intuition about what will best serve the client. Four to five hours of sitting in front of a computer screen is not easy (unless you are on MDMA!). However, the sincerity of the client and the "contact high" I often get from working with someone on MDMA makes the time fly. Creating psychological breakthroughs for someone else is truly an honor and a privilege.

PART II

USING MDMA THERAPY FOR VARIOUS CONDITIONS

In this section, each chapter discusses how to use MDMA to help specific conditions people would like to overcome. You'll learn how this cutting-edge therapy can assist people to overcome trauma, depression, anxiety, couple's issues, and even accelerate spiritual growth.

REPORTS OF
MY BEING
ALIVE AND WELL
HAVE BEEN
GROSSLY EXAGGERATED.

© BRILLIANT
ENTERPRISES
1970

CHAPTER 6

WORKING WITH TRAUMA AND PTSD

"Short-term MDMA therapy has demonstrated transforma-
tive effects, offering new possibilities for effective and efficient
treatment of PTSD."

— Katie Brown, psychiatrist.com

Post-Traumatic Stress Disorder, better known as PTSD, is now a term most people have become familiar with in recent years. After World War I, it was commonly called "shell shock." After World War II, it was known as "battle fatigue." Yet, PTSD is not just something that happens to veterans. Whatever its various terms, PTSD symptoms have always been much the same.

Common symptoms include:

1. Vivid flashbacks of past traumatic events
2. Intrusive thoughts or images leading to much anxiety
3. Nightmares
4. Intense distress at real or symbolic reminders of the trauma
5. Physical sensations such as pain, sweating, nausea, or trembling

PTSD and trauma are more common than you may think. According to the CDC, one in five children is sexually molested, one in four women experience attempted or completed rape, and 35% of couples engage in physical violence. That's a lot of people. For a long time, folks suffered in silence or were prescribed anti-depressants to help tone down their symptoms. But times have changed. When Harvard studies indicated people with PTSD also suffered from increased risk of cancer and heart disease, the medical field began to take notice.[7]

Then, as books such as "The Body Keeps the Score" topped the *New York Times* bestseller list, more people realized their anxiety and neuroses may be the result of early trauma.

Besides doing my Master's thesis on the effects of MDMA on PTSD, I've seen a lot of clients suffering from its many symptoms. In my experience, nothing works as fast as MDMA-assisted therapy for treating trauma. It seems that even the FDA agrees. Extensive clinical trials indicate that MDMA-assisted therapy is so effective that it will soon become a legally prescribed drug for the treatment of PTSD. What's even more remarkable is that, in the clinical trials, not much "talk therapy" took place. While on MDMA, blindfolded patients mostly just listened to music. Most of the "talk therapy" happened between MDMA sessions. The FDA trials were geared mainly toward evaluating whether a simple pill in a supportive environment could cure PTSD.

Of course, every medicine for the psyche achieves better results when traditional therapeutic interventions are included. For example, anti-depressants work much better when they are used in conjunction with talk therapy. The same applies to people taking MDMA in conjunction with various therapeutic interventions. My personal experience would

---

[7] https://www.hsph.harvard.edu/news/press-releases/ptsd-linked-to-increased-risk-of-ovar-ian-cancer/#:~:text=Boston%2C%20MA%20%E2%80%93%20Women%20who%20experienced,School%20of%20Public%20Health%20and

indicate that, when therapy is combined with MDMA, the success rate with PTSD is over 90% as measured by self-report two months later. Some of these clients have had PTSD for over 30 years! When I started working with people suffering from PTSD, I found the results astonishing and deeply emotional to witness.

So, what is it like when a client who has PTSD does talk therapy while on MDMA? Well, it depends on the client, the therapist, and the therapeutic interventions used during the session. In the rest of this chapter, I'll discuss a few types of interventions that I've found helpful and why they work so well. But first, it's important to distinguish between PTSD and other types of traumas.

PTSD and Related Conditions

PTSD usually refers to a condition that patients have in which a traumatic event is so severe that it greatly interferes with their daily functioning. In recent years, many people have talked about experiencing trauma, but in most cases, they refer to less dramatic events. Having your best friend's head blown off while you're next to them is a cause for PTSD; having your mother spank you intensely once when you were a child, while unpleasant, would likely be referred to as "simple trauma." Having your mother spank and yell at you every week for many years would probably be termed "complex trauma." Complex trauma occurs when a child is exposed to multiple traumatic events over a long period of time—often of an interpersonal nature.

While psychologists use different terms depending on the severity and frequency of a person's trauma, it's essential to realize that trauma is in the eye of the beholder. For instance, I once had a client with severe PTSD symptoms due to a single time of seeing his dad yell at his mom. On the other hand, I've seen a client that, as far as I could tell, apparently had no trauma symptoms after witnessing his mate being murdered. Somehow, his religious beliefs assured him she was "in a better place," and he was okay with that. People react to things very differently. Yet, in general, PTSD and simple trauma (mostly one-time events) are easier to overcome than the effects of complex trauma. When I interview a client who seems to be suffering from complex trauma, I expect it may take many talk therapy sessions, along with more than one MDMA journey, to get lasting results.

A frequent problem related to trauma is that of panic attacks. Panic attacks are commonly defined as a brief episode of intense anxiety which causes the physical sensations of fear. MDMA-assisted therapy can also be a very effective and quick way of helping people with this condition. Panic attacks are most often triggered by some traumatic event. Therefore, the same therapies that help with PTSD (including MDMA therapy), tend to work with overcoming panic attacks. Unfortunately, many people suffering from trauma or panic attacks never get the help they could benefit from. Even when they do seek help, most people are simply prescribed an anti-depressant or anti-anxiety medication—neither of which work very well and mostly lessen symptoms. In the next section, I will briefly describe several easy interventions that work in conjunction with MDMA. By reading about these methods, I hope you'll be inspired to get help for yourself or someone you love who suffers from trauma-based conditions.

The Trauma Healing Helpers

When a client comes to me complaining of trauma, I first see what they've done in the past to help with their symptoms. If they're on anti-depressants, we decide if slowly weaning off them (or reducing them as discussed in Chapter 2) in preparation for an MDMA journey is what they'd like to try. Then, I seek to ascertain which of the three categories of trauma they best fall into. Finally, after completing a thorough intake form, we settle on a day for their journey. While I occasionally see people in my office, I always see victims of sexual abuse over Zoom. After all, if you've experienced trauma due to being raped, going to a stranger's office and taking a drug is not the safest environment for healing. The clear boundaries and comfort created via Zoom sessions work much better.

In my work with traumatized clients, I usually begin by trying to instill skills that I feel are helpful in their healing. Those valuable skills can best be described as curiosity, discovery, and specificity. Typically, trauma victims attempt to avoid or distract themselves from their trauma symptoms. Instead, I advise my clients to get curious about them. For example, what triggers their symptoms? Where do they feel the symptoms in their body? How would they describe their symptoms in terms of sensations? How long do they last? Such curiosity inevitably leads to the second attitude: discovery.

I want my clients to discover ever new subtleties about their trauma reactions. What events trigger their symptoms, and which do not? The more clients can engage their "inner Sherlock Holmes," the better. When a person's prefrontal cortex is involved, that's half the battle. Finally, the third skill I want clients to engage with is the ability to be very specific. Most trauma survivors know very few specifics about the originating event. Instead, they have dutifully avoided it as best they can. Yet, under the influence of MDMA, I encourage clients to repeatedly go over every detail they can about their trauma, from their thoughts and feelings to the images and sounds they perceive. Such repetition and attention to detail tend to have the effect of neutralizing their trauma. Fortunately, the medicine makes all this relatively painless and easy to do.

A lot of the healing that results from various types of trauma work is the pairing of traumatic experiences with a newfound sense of safety, relaxation, and impartiality. As my clients calmly and safely describe their traumatic events while under the influence of MDMA, new and healing associations are being made. At its core, trauma occurs when an event is so intense that there isn't time or the emotional resources to properly process what happened. Having clients repeatedly describe their trauma while feeling comfortable and safe allows them to fully "digest" the original traumatic event. Once that occurs, their symptoms tend to either significantly lessen or disappear.

Charles, an Iraq war veteran, came to me complaining of nightmares and difficulty falling asleep. He didn't think of himself as having PTSD, but it was clear to me that trauma was the culprit. I suggested he do an MDMA journey, and somewhat reluctantly, he agreed. I was curious and a little apprehensive as to what might happen. Well, the five-hour session was never dull. I felt like I was doing brain surgery as Charles reported a flood of insights, emotions, and violent images. Charles reported he hadn't felt much of anything since his best friend was killed in Iraq while he watched helplessly. I had him enter a peaceful state and slowly go through the images that had haunted him at night. Over time, his energy shifted from fear and anger to grief and self-compassion. He cried for a long time, then finally seemed at peace.

I emailed Charles the next day–like I do with all my clients–to see how he was doing. He quickly emailed me back, saying he had slept better than he had in years. He reported being exhausted, but somehow in a good way–like he'd endured an "internal workout." A week later, during our integration session, Charles said he'd had no more nightmares. We reviewed some exercises to help him get out his anger safely when it would quickly arise. Four months later, Charles contacted me for another journey. This time, instead of having traumatic events from his past show up, he focused on opening up to more love with his wife and compassion for himself. After that second session, Charles reported, "That drug profoundly healed me. That medicine saved my life." When he told me that, we both got teary eyed.

The Mocking Movie Method

There are various techniques that can help trauma victims quickly overcome their bad memories and release their symptoms. When used with

MDMA, some methods can often cure a person's symptoms in record time. One of my favorite techniques is The Mocking Movie Method (MMM). In my practice, I've witnessed people who have suffered from flashbacks and anxiety for years eradicate their trauma reaction in five minutes. Before explaining the specifics of this method, it's helpful to understand why it works so well.

When a person is traumatized, their mind often tries to process what happened by repeatedly going over the event. Unfortunately, this can often result in a "trauma loop" in which the repeated disturbing images just keep triggering more anxiety and other symptoms. To interrupt this cycle, I tell my clients that we must alter and preferably neutralize the traumatic memory. I explain that if the memory were likened to being on a DVD (remember those?), we want to take a nail to that DVD and scratch it up until it can't be played again. Then, if their brain attempts to play the memory, it simply won't play–at least not in a disturbing manner. To accomplish this "nail to a DVD," we imagine the originating event as a movie, but we make the movie as ridiculous as possible.

When given a choice between remembering a highly disturbing event and imagining a highly bizarre scenario, the human mind will tend to go with the bizarre one. Thus, I tell my clients to begin their Mocking Movie Method by creating a mini movie of the originating trauma scene, but to play it in their head in very fast motion. Then, once they reach the end of this "movie" in their head, to play that movie in reverse very quickly. The whole forward and backward reenactment of their trauma should take no more than 30 seconds. Once they've done this, I tell them to give all the people in their movie big Mickey Mouse ears and a Bozo nose while they, once again, play the scene in fast motion–forward and reverse.

By now, many of my clients are smiling as they create their ridiculous mental movie. But wait, there's more! I have them see their movie again, forward and reverse, but this time the antagonist slips on a banana peel and slides into a big pile of shit. Finally, I have them view the movie again, but this time they're free to add whatever ridiculous and creative touches they would like. Once that's done, I suggest they "try to see the original trauma, but this time notice how all kinds of bizarre images keep showing up for you—even if you don't try." That suggestion and their recent mental conditioning are usually enough to turn their formerly traumatic memories into a ridiculous and harmless scene. The scariness of their trauma has been magically neutralized.

Mary, a 63-year-old woman, had been raped when she was 18. Unfortunately, she never got over it. She often had nightmares about it and told me, "I have rarely slept through the night ever since." Her trauma reaction had generalized to being afraid of intimacy and never genuinely enjoying sex. Years of talk therapy had done little to alleviate her symptoms. Amazingly, all this changed for her in a single MDMA session. The combination of fully "digesting" the details of the rape in a safe emotional environment and the Mocking Movie Method completely cured her of her long-lasting symptoms. She could hardly believe it. Seeing how effective this approach is with dozens of clients, I wasn't surprised. Sometimes all you need to get over years of being stuck is a really good technique and an amazing medicine.

From Fear to Freedom

When working with PTSD, or any fearful reaction to past or current events, it's possible to teach people to have a new relationship with fear. Franklin Delano Roosevelt once said, "The only thing we have to fear is fear itself." I agree. The problem is people are so afraid of fear that they come up with many ways to avoid it—including developing symptoms that both distract them and create new problems. Yet, by teaching people how to better handle and let go of fear, all this can be avoided. Fortunately, such a skill can easily be taught—especially while a person is on MDMA. MDMA has been shown to decrease blood flow to the

Amygdala–thereby helping people feel safe and relaxed even while thinking about traumatic events.

I instruct my clients to develop a new way of being with fear by first describing it as a particular type of "relationship." For most of my clients, their relationship with fear could best be described as fear being their tormentor, and they are the helpless victim. That doesn't feel good. I explain that they are in a mental prison if, whenever fear shows its face, they become paralyzed or run in the opposite direction. Instead, I suggest they become better acquainted with fear, and even attempt to become interested in it and friendly with it. When fear arises, greet it with the words, "Hello fear...wassup? What would you like me to know?" Such an approach allows one to gradually see that most fears are paper tigers.

Once a person has a different attitude toward their fear, I offer a simple guided meditation that helps them see their fear from a broader perspective. Below is an exercise I borrowed from spiritual author and teacher Loch Kelly. This guided meditation can quickly help one go from fully identifying with a fear, to having fear not be a problem.

Disidentifying with Fear Exercise:

1. Think of something or someone that brings up fear in you. Allow yourself to feel the fear as you think to yourself, "I am afraid."

2. Next, as you feel the sensations of fear in your body, say to yourself, "I am aware of feeling fear." Notice how this new phrase changes how you relate to the fear you're feeling.

3. Next, as you feel the sensations of fear in your body, notice that these sensations exist within a larger field of spacious awareness. Perhaps feeling the space around your body can help with this.

4. Then, as best you can, relax into your spacious awareness and think to yourself, "As this spacious awareness, fear is allowed and even welcomed."

5. Finally, say the phrase, "Awareness and fear are not separate." See how this feels or resonates in your body.

If you use this five-step exercise when dealing with fear (or any uncomfortable feeling), you can change your orientation to that emotion. Once you're not fully identified and resisting your experience, it can more easily pass through you like clouds moving through an empty sky. It's a great realization and capability to allow any uncomfortable feeling to pass through you quickly and easily. Such an ability instantly increases one's sense of inner peace and wholeness.

Internal Family Systems

A recent approach to working with trauma is what is known as the Internal Family Systems (IFS) approach. In this modality, clients are taught that, inside themselves, a whole family of various "parts" exists; each has its own viewpoint, personality, and desires. This cutting-edge method aims to create a dialog with one or more parts that create problems in one's life. For example, suppose a person has a part that is terrified of physical intimacy. In that case, the therapist will gently ask that part what its goals are, what it needs to feel safe, and if it can find a new way of behaving that does not interfere with the client's life.

When I do IFS with trauma victims, I notice that there is usually a "protector" part that causes a lot of the client's symptoms. This protective part aims to keep the client safe, but often the way it goes about that task keeps the traumatized part stuck in the past. While on MDMA, I have a dialog with all the key parts, and eventually we negotiate new ways of behaving that will work better for everyone. It's very effective work. To learn more about IFS and even understand how to use it on yourself, I recommend the book, "Self-Therapy" by Jay Early. Yet, this type of therapy can be both subtle and complex. If possible, I recommend exploring it with a therapist who is practiced in this technique.

From Blame and Shame to a Positive Reframe

When working with any client suffering from trauma, the final intervention I like to do is to reframe what happened in a more positive light. The meaning we give to an event is as important as what happened. By placing traumatic events within an empowering context, it allows clients to forgive themselves or their perpetrators more easily.

I'll give a personal example. As a child, my stepfather used to beat me periodically with a belt. He had quite a temper, and if I "talked back" to him, he would beat me up again. This led to me running away from home at age 12, but eventually the police found me and brought me back to–you guessed it–another beating. In those days (the early 70s) there was less awareness around the issue of child abuse, so I had few options other than to just endure his occasional rages. Of course, for many years I carried many physical and mental scars from these events– including a deep hatred for my stepfather.

Then, in my thirties, I decided to take MDMA and focus on what my stepfather had done to me. I had anticipated a lot of anger and catharsis would show up, but that's not what happened. Instead, I saw my stepfather as a deeply wounded soul who could only feel empowered when he was beating up on his step kids. I had also blamed myself for not fighting back, but on MDMA, I could forgive myself. Finally, I saw the whole scenario as something that had made me strong internally and led me to seek inner peace from a young age. Tears of gratitude flowed from my eyes as I reframed the whole relationship as one that had empowered me to grow strong in the face of adversity. When people ask me how I've been able to write so many books and meet so many spiritual leaders, I often answer, "My stepfather inspired me from a young age to persevere no matter what." And the best part is, I really feel gratitude now when I think of my stepfather.

My story is not unique. We all have faced plenty of adversity in our lives. I tell my clients that life challenges are like going to the gym and lifting weights. When we work out, we lift weights to grow stronger. When adversity comes along, depending on how we look at and handle that challenge, we can grow stronger or become crushed. Most of the spiritual leaders I've interviewed–from Oprah and Mother Teresa to the Dalai Lama–have experienced a lot of traumas. Yet, they used those traumatic events to grow spiritually stronger. They used their challenges to develop more peace, compassion, and resilience. There is no getting around adversity and trauma in human life. However, with the help of things like MDMA, various therapeutic techniques, and reframing, such experiences can often help us deepen our humanity.

There are many other modalities for treating trauma that have, in clinical studies, shown promise. For example, EMDR (Eye Movement Desensitization and Reprocessing), CBT (Cognitive Behavioral Therapy), and PE (Prolonged Exposure Therapy). Each of these can work well when used with a trained therapist. If you or someone you love noticeably suffers from trauma, I encourage you to seek a therapist trained in any of these modalities. In my experience, each of these methods works even better under the influence of MDMA, but studies to prove that are only now being started.

Once again, in this chapter, I have poured a lot of specific information your way. The good news is that MDMA-assisted therapy can offer people a quick, effective, and inexpensive way to overcome trauma-related challenges. ...and having a simple way to let go of fear and tap into more love is truly priceless...

CHAPTER 7

KEYS TO OVERCOMING ANXIETY

*"MDMA taught me that happiness is not a destination,
but a state of being that we can access within ourselves."*

— Amanda Sage, author

MDMA is a bit like a Swiss Army Knife. It can do several things, and it can do many of them very well when taken under favorable conditions. One of the things I've often focused on with my clients is how to use the insights from MDMA to reduce their worry or anxiety. Approximately 31% of U.S. adults experience an anxiety disorder sometime in their lives. I used to be one of those people. Anxiety runs in my family. In fact, it practically gallops! As a teen, besides being depressed for a while, I was also anxious. I frequently ruminated about how I might say something stupid. Eventually, this led me to hardly talk at all. When being unable to speak became unbearable, I began reading books about hypnosis and meditation to overcome my condition. Fortunately, such things helped, so when I became a psychotherapist, I often focused on helping people with anxiety disorders.

Anxiety is defined as a feeling of fear, dread, or uneasiness. Along with uncomfortable feelings, there is usually an intense focus on counterproductive thoughts. Psychologists often say frequent anxiety results from difficult experiences in childhood, adolescence, or adulthood. Signs of an anxiety disorder include:

1. worrying that is uncontrollable and causes distress.
2. worrying that affects your daily life, including school, your job, and your social life.
3. the inability to let go of your worries.
4. the tendency to worry about all sorts of things, such as your job or health, and minor concerns, such as household chores.

There are several things you can try to combat anxiety, including:

Cognitive Behavioral Therapy
Deep breathing
Exercise
Journaling
Meditation
Reading
Socializing with friends
Speaking with your health care provider
Limiting caffeine intake
Prioritizing getting a good night's sleep

Find What Works

Each of the methods listed above can be quite helpful, and each has its place in combating anxiety. Yet, I have a simple rule as a therapist: find out what the client can do that, in their direct experience, makes them quickly feel better. Then, teach that person a simple method that will allow them to feel better consistently in their daily life. Unfortunately, this approach is unusual. We've all heard the adage, "If all you have is a hammer, everything starts to look like a nail." I have found that many therapists fall into this trap.

Psychotherapists get rewarded for becoming highly specialized in their field. Then, as clients come to them, they treat them with the best method and approach they know. In fact, there is often value in this way of doing things. After all, you want a therapist that is an expert in what they know how to do. However, I've used a different approach. I've become somewhat knowledgeable about many different techniques—and an expert in none (except MDMA therapy). In that way, I can offer many approaches for a client—and through their experience on MDMA, see what works best for them.

When a client comes to me for anxiety issues, in our initial Zoom session, I try to get a sense of what may be causing it. Is it due to trauma? Might it run in the family and be partly due to genetics? How are their sleep, caffeine intake, or stress levels? If I can guess the leading cause of their anxiety, I can often make an educated guess as to what approach will greatly help them. Fortunately, while a client is on MDMA, it's easy to ascertain if a method I give them truly works for them. Sometimes we'll try three or four approaches before one method clearly speaks to them in a way that is immediately impactful. Once I see that, we dive even deeper into the technique that works for them.

The various approaches and methods for combating anxiety can be categorized in many ways. For simplicity's sake, I've learned to classify anti-anxiety strategies into three different categories. I label these three groups:

1. Methods of Reassurance
2. Methods of Sensory Presence
3. Methods of Disidentification

While I have a client on MDMA, I will often try a method that falls under each of these three approaches. The information I previously gathered from our one-hour Zoom call will usually give me a hint of what approach will work best, but my guesswork is often wrong. That's why trying different methods while on MDMA is so valuable. The medicine seems to speed up the clarity as to what works for a given individual and what just leaves them feeling anxious and confused. So, without further ado, I will expound on the three approaches for combating anxiety, including examples of simple methods that fall into each category.

The Methods of Reassurance:

Anxiety is really the result of fear. The fear might be due to the fear of failure, loss, disapproval, overwhelm, or a myriad of other things. Whatever the source, a helpful antidote is reassuring one's mind that things are okay. Cognitive Behavioral Therapy, CBT, is perhaps the most researched and used approach for reducing anxiety. It primarily consists of teaching clients to correct cognitive "distortions" such as catastrophizing, generalizing, or discounting the positive. When a person's thoughts are distorted, their emotions also become distorted. So, what replaces these cognitive distortions? Essentially, thoughts that better align with reality and/or help to reassure a person that things aren't as bad as they may seem.

For example, suppose a client focuses too much attention on an unimportant detail (magnification) or something unlikely to happen. In that case, a therapist might have them focus on the big picture, or what is most likely to occur. If a client generalizes that "I always fail at things," a therapist might have them focus on things they have succeeded at. When I work with someone on MDMA, I'll gently point out their cognitive distortions, then ask them to come up with a phrase that powerfully refutes their anxiety-provoking thoughts. When the client, under the influence of the medicine, comes up with a phrase that feels good to them, it has a lasting impact. For a technique to be truly effective, it must be more than just an intellectual understanding. It must be able to be used in daily life, and a simple phrase with an emotional resonance seems to do the trick.

Here's a brief transcript of a client, Robert, exploring how he came up with a way to overcome his tendency to catastrophize in his head:

> **JR:** So, Robert, what do you think keeps you from this peace you're feeling now? What keeps you locked up in worry so much of the time?
>
> **Robert:** There's so much to worry about…Global warming could kill off half of humanity, and what if I lose my job and end up homeless?
>
> **JR:** When you think of worse-case scenarios like you just expressed, I call that "catastrophizing." Apparently, it's something your mind does a lot. What might you say to yourself when you catastrophize that would help you let go of your worry and feel more peaceful?
>
> **Robert:** I don't know….
>
> **JR:** Well, go inside now and try to intuit something you could say that would reassure you that things will be okay. It could be a simple phrase like, "It's gonna be alright," or, "There's really no need to worry now." Just imagine what would work to hear at those times you're locked in "what if" scenarios.
>
> **Robert:** (as he closes his eyes, a very long pause, then excitedly). I got it! I need to hear, "I've always been able to handle things." That's true. I always rise to the challenge. That's what I need to hear!
>
> **JR:** That's great. Fantastic. As you think of losing your job now, try that phrase…
>
> **Robert:** (long pause). It works! It's like that thought no longer had any legs to stand on.

JR: Great. Next week when we do our integration session, I'll remind you of that phrase, and give you a way to remember to use it in your daily life.

I have found that when a client intuits a helpful phrase while on MDMA, and tries it out in response to anxious thoughts, they can immediately ascertain if it works. If it does, it's like discovering a dear friend who will be there for them for the rest of their lives. Sometimes, I'll suggest phrases or affirmations if they have trouble coming up with their own. Interestingly, most of the time clients will slightly alter what I come up with so it more fully resonates with them. For example, I recently suggested to a client the affirmation, "I can handle failure and rejection. It's not the end of the world." Yet, she countered, "That doesn't quite do it for me." Then her face lit up and she blurted out, "I'm *learning* to handle failure and rejection like it's no big deal. That works for me!"

I congratulated her for coming up with what resonated, and in our integration session, she affirmed that her phrase was working better than she had even hoped for.

There are other methods that I place in the category of reassurance. The IFS approach I briefly described in the last chapter can help provide empathy and reassurance to a part of a person that feels anxious. In addition, even certain meditations can be a way of creating a feeling of comfort. At my podcast website, AwarenessExplorers.com, in the navigation bar is the word "Meditations." There you can find over 100 free guided meditations from some of the most well-known spiritual teachers on the planet–such as Byron Katie, Deepak Chopra, Marianne Williamson, and Adyashanti. Most of these meditations are about ten minutes long, and many offer a soothing, peaceful way folks can access the peace and safety within. For example, I'll often lead a guided meditation such as the following:

Reassurance of Love Meditation

Relax comfortably and, when you're ready, close your eyes. Take a couple of deep breaths. Now think of a person, a child, or a beloved pet that you have great affection for. Remember special times with this being– times you felt particularly connected to them. (Long pause). Feel your care and love for them in your heart and allow yourself to feel grateful for how they are part of your life. (Long pause). If it helps, you can imagine hugging or holding them in a way that helps you to feel even more connected. (Long pause). Imagine telling them how much they mean to you and seeing how your words make them very happy. (Long pause). Once again, allow yourself to feel grateful for their being in your life. (Long pause). Feel the peace and safety of feeling connected in your heart. (Long pause). When you're ready, gently come back to the room and very slowly begin to open your eyes.

I have found the preceding guided meditation very helpful for people suffering from anxiety. Excessive worry is partly due to having too much focus or energy in one's head. By bringing one's focus and energy into one's heart, it's as if worrying thoughts lose their appeal. With this guided meditation, in just two or three minutes, a person can shift their energy away from worry and instead feel the safety and connection inherent in their heart. If you experience a lot of anxiety occasionally, try slowly recording these words into your smartphone–then playing them back when your mind becomes overactive. I think you'll find it works amazingly well in a short period of time.

The Sensory Approach:

A second way to let go of anxiety and become more present is what I call the Sensory Approach. It consists of various methods that all focus on one or more of the senses. In many meditation traditions, people are instructed to focus on one of the 5 senses to get "out of one's head" and into one's body. The sensations of the body are always present in this present moment. By turning your attention to the senses, thoughts and anxiety are crowded out of your awareness.

Different people have an affinity for turning to different senses. Some people like to focus on body sensations–such as how one's breath feels at the tip of one's nose. Other people find that listening to all the subtle sounds around them helps them feel more present and reduce their anxiety. One method that makes use of various senses is to focus on answering three questions:

1. What are 3 things I can see and appreciate in my physical environment?
2. What are 3 sounds I can hear, and which one is the softest?
3. What are 3 places in my body that feel uncomfortable or tense, and 3 places that feel relaxed or good?

As a person answers these three questions, they inevitably become more present to their current sensations and less present to the swirling thoughts in their head.

The first time I was on national TV (on CNN), this sensory approach to curtailing anxiety saved me from massive embarrassment. As the producer was attaching the microphone to me, he told me the guest after me had been delayed, so I would have 14 minutes to fill–instead of four minutes. This information–two minutes before being live to 3 million people–sent me into overwhelming anxiety. My thoughts started to spin out of control. Fortunately, I had a remedy. I began feeling the sensations of the bottom of my feet. Instead of focusing on my thoughts, I focused on how my feet felt. When thoughts would creep in, I would drown them out by hearing myself sing in my head, "Twist and Shout" by the Beatles. The combination of focusing on the sensations of my feet and the sound of the Beatles helped me to stay present. When the camera light went on, I felt relaxed and confident.

The Disidentification Approach

I label the third approach to overcoming anxiety with the word "dis-identification." What that means is any method that creates mental or emotional distance between "you" and the anxious thoughts swirling around in your head. We all have a certain relationship with fear, and for many people, the relationship is one where fear is the master, and they are the servant. That must change if a person ever hopes to be free of anxiety. While on MDMA, people tend to be much less identified with their anxiety, so I use that as an opportunity for them to practice not identifying with their thoughts.

As a teen, I often ruminated that I might say something stupid. These ruminations soon led me to rarely talk. Fortunately, I read a book about an interesting antidote to my worrying thoughts. The book stated we usually identify with whatever thoughts go through our brains because of the consistent tone of the voice inside our heads. We take the tone of the voice we hear to be our true selves. Yet, if you change the tone of your inner dialogue, it soon becomes apparent that the thoughts swirling around your brain are just programming from your past–and not "you." In fact, many of those thoughts are self-destructive and were implanted by dysfunctional parents or teachers.

The specific technique this book suggested was to, when thinking counterproductive thoughts, change the *tone* of the voice inside your head. The author suggested making the tone sound ridiculous, such as sounding like Mickey Mouse, or Bugs Bunny. My previous thoughts of "You better not say that!" used to be heard inside my head as an urgent demand that my life was in danger if I said something stupid. Now, hearing, "You better not say that" in the high-pitched squeal of Mickey Mouse or the irreverent tone of Bugs Bunny just made me smile. I could no longer take such thoughts so seriously. They lost virtually all their power to impact me. In essence, I no longer identified with these counterproductive thoughts, and with the lack of identification, they gradually faded away.

When we are no longer identified with anxious thoughts, they naturally lose their energy. In the previous chapter on PTSD, I offered the "Disidentification with Fear" meditation. That's another simple method that uses the power of not taking one's thoughts so seriously. Rather than try to stop one's thoughts–which is almost impossible to do, I guide my clients to see their thoughts more objectively while on MDMA. It can be a breakthrough for clients to recognize they can have worrying thoughts go through their brains and not be affected by them. Once they have such an experience with MDMA, it's like giving them an invisible shield they can use to protect themselves from their anxious thoughts.

When on MDMA, I've noticed that people have clearer access to knowing when a technique resonates with them. As I guide clients through the various approaches to reducing their anxiety, they report to me what worked and what did not. Often, I'll ask them to rate their level of peace on a 1 to 10 scale, with 10 being entirely peaceful and 1 being terribly anxious. With each method I guide them through, we can see what worked well, what worked a little, and what did not resonate at all. Then, when we do the integration session a week later, I know what methods to focus on for maximal impact.

In the stressful world in which we live, the ability to quiet one's anxiety is a critical life skill. Unfortunately, it's usually not taught in school. With the help of MDMA and an organized approach to finding the specific methods that work for a given individual, great progress can be made in a single day. When I do this work with clients, they often report that it feels miraculous. Many have described how it's as if a whole new world opens up for them. Going from a noisy mind to one that's often quiet and at ease is like healing someone from cancer that eats away at their soul. MDMA therapy and a good anti-anxiety technique can give people suffering from anxiety a deeper taste of freedom and love than they may have ever thought possible.

CHAPTER 8

ECSTASY AS A DEPRESSION HELPER

"It (MDMA) takes away the feelings of self-hatred and con-demnation, which are the biggest obstacles to insight...For reasons we don't understand, MDMA allows people to do this, typically in one (psychotherapeutic) session."

— Ann Shulgin, author

Depression is becoming an epidemic in modern society. The rate of clinical depression has increased by 500% in the last 50 years. Suicides, overdose fatalities, and just plain feeling "blah" are all too common nowadays. Can MDMA help with "the blues?" Ongoing research says it can, but more research is needed.[8]

MDMA is not a magic pill that will help you overcome sadness, grief, and depression. Unlike anti-depressants which are often touted as a pill that cures depression, MDMA is best taken in a therapeutic context. Unfortunately, much of the world has been sold on the idea that a pill is all that's needed. Anti-depressants are a 20 billion dollar-a-year

---

[8] https://www.medicalnewstoday.com/articles/mdma-depression

industry, and yet studies show that for mild and moderate depression, they are only 1% more effective than placebos in most cases.

Many people coming to me for journey work are depressed. They know something is wrong but don't know exactly what it is. An MDMA session is almost always helpful in pinpointing their most significant issues, and then helping them gain insight into what they need to do to move forward. Regrettably, I can't immediately do a session with most of the folks coming to me with depression. It ends up that most of them are taking SSRI-type anti-depressants, and such medicines interfere with the effects of MDMA. As stated in Chapter 2, I have such folks gradually wean themselves to get off (or to a lower dose) of anti-depressants before I suggest they take MDMA. People taking SSRIs should consult their doctor before reducing their medication.

For people who are ready to take MDMA for depression-type symptoms, I do a thorough intake. The more I know about them before their journey, the better. Depression is not a simple, one size fits all mental health condition. There are many reasons why folks get depressed. About 20% of adult Americans are on an anti-depressant and/or consider themselves depressed. Several years ago, when I realized the extent of the problem, I teamed up with a famous medical doctor, Emmett Miller, to create a program called "From Sad to Glad: How to Overcome Stress, Anxiety, and Depression and Feel Happy Again." It's a 6-hour audio program with a 50-page workbook and 12 guided meditations. We initially sold it for $299, but when Covid hit, we decided to offer it for free to anyone who wanted to download it. You can use this link to access it for yourself or anyone you know who might want it: https://www.fromsad2glad.com/thank-you/

It's a great program. If you or someone you love is depressed, get it! After all, it's now free...

There are many theories as to why folks get depressed. As I share in my book, "The Enlightenment Project: How I Went From Depressed to Blessed, and You Can Too," I was suicidally depressed as a teen. Nowadays, in America, about 48,000 people die of suicide each year. I was almost one of those casualties. I would come home from school each day and think of ways to kill myself. I finally set a date to do the deed—by jumping off a bridge, but my plan was interrupted two days before my "suicide date." On that day, Mr. Downing, my 8th grade English teacher, asked me to stay after class. I figured I was in trouble, but I didn't know what for. It really didn't matter. After all, I figured I only had a couple more days to live.

When the class was all cleared out of students, Mr. Downing told me to have a seat. I refused to look at him because I knew he had penetrating eyes. After a long silence, he finally spoke. He said, "Jonathan, I sense that you're feeling really, really bad right now, but I want you to know how much I care about you. You're a good kid and very smart, and you have a sensitive heart. I don't know what exactly is going on, but I know that if you can make it through this rough patch, you're going to have an amazing life. I just want you to know that. You might be feeling hopeless now, but that's going to change. You're special in ways you may not be able to see now, but I can see it. I want you to know that I'm here for you if you ever need someone to talk to."

Tears flowed from my eyes as I listened to Mr. Downing's words. I was too afraid to reveal to him my plan to end my life, but before leaving his classroom, I hugged Mr. Downing and thanked him for his caring. That night, I decided I'd put off my plan to kill myself. Years later, I was able to thank Mr. Downing in person for saving my life. When he heard how he had saved my life, we both cried....If someone you know could benefit from hearing how much you care about them, I encourage you to speak up. You never know...you may be saving their life.

When I was a teen, my depression was triggered by a feeling of loss and powerlessness. My family had just moved to a new area, and I had no friends and felt overwhelmed. In addition, on a regular basis, my stepfather would beat me up. Loss is part of human life, but we're never taught how to handle it effectively. Fortunately, MDMA can often help. I've led many MDMA trips for people who are dealing with the issue of loss. Their depression can come from a divorce, a breakup, a loved one's death, the ending of a job, or even the loss of a certain dream. Whatever the loss, MDMA can give folks a larger perspective on their lives. In such cases, I have people face their grief more directly. Often, a person's inability to fully feel their grief keeps them in a low-level depression for a long time. Once they fully feel or "digest" their loss (with the help of MDMA), a space opens up for moving forward in their life.

For clients suffering from loss and grief, I often give them a useful analogy. If you're an acrobat on a flying trapeze, holding on to a swinging trapeze is your lifeline. Yet, to move forward, you need to let go of the trapeze you're holding onto to grab the next swinging trapeze. This is hard to do because, at some point, you'll be in mid-air holding on to nothing. However, with a bit of faith and skill, you'll soon be safely grabbing the next swinging trapeze. For many folks suffering from depression, they are either too afraid to let go of what they've been holding onto, or they're unclear whether there will ever be another trapeze to reach for. MDMA can help with both situations. When skillfully guided, MDMA can help someone let go of what's gone and help them see and create a vision of a meaningful and worthwhile future.

Internal Exercises for Depression

My dad worked hard all his life to retire at age 58. A couple of months before retiring, he found himself surprisingly tired. After my insistence, he finally went to see his doctor. He found out he was suffering from stage 4 Lymphoma—and was given six months to live. My dad fell into a deep depression. Although my dad wasn't into what he called "weird stuff," he asked for my advice. I suggested I guide him on an MDMA session, and he agreed. During the session, he directly faced his fear of dying—but powerfully decided he wanted to do whatever it took to live.

I helped him create a vision of exactly what he wanted to do with more time, and I had him visualize such experiences. By helping him with hypnosis, various supplements, and his doctor's chemotherapy treatments, I'm proud to say my dad lived 17 more years before finally succumbing to Lymphoma.

One of the things I suggested my dad do to help restore his will to live was what I call the *Six Months to Live* exercise. I've used this with many of my clients who feel a lack of excitement for life or are depressed. It's a simple exercise. I give people 3 minutes to write down everything they'd want to do if they only had six months to live. I tell them to be as specific as possible. For example, they shouldn't say, "I'd travel." Instead, I suggest they write down exactly where they might want to go, whom they'd want to go with, and how long they would want to be there. Once their list is complete, I suggest they start doing some of the things on their list.

With six months left to live, people do what's most important to them. Depressed folks often have a lack of meaning in their lives, or a lack of excitement about their future. Frequently doing things that bring meaning and delight back into their lives makes them feel better. This is not rocket science. However, the sad fact is that many people know what to do, but few people are motivated enough to do what they know. With the clarity that comes from an MDMA session, along with the support offered in an integration session, many people can climb out of a depression that they've known for far too long.

Another approach I use to assist people with depression is to help them get clear about the *type* of person they want to be. An easy way to do this is to help them figure out what they'd like to be known for by the time they die. Along these lines, I once read a true story about a man named Alfred who had the unusual experience of reading his own obituary in the newspaper. It ends up Alfred's *brother* had died, and the coroner mistakenly thought it was Alfred. To Alfred's surprise, his obituary stated that he was known as the "merchant of death" and that he had become wealthy through the killing and mutilation of thousands of people. Well, Alfred was horrified to read this scathing obituary. Knowing that he was not truly dead, he asked himself a life-changing question that changed the world. Alfred asked himself, "What would I *like* to be known for by the time I really die?"

Since Alfred was a man of means, he came up with some lofty goals. He mused that he'd like to be known for great achievements in science, literature, and even world peace. So, Alfred---last name Nobel, started the Nobel Prizes. To this day, the Nobel Prizes are funded through the profits of the company he founded—which sells dynamite. By getting clear about what he'd like to be known for by the time he died, Alfred was able to create a life of meaning for himself and a lasting legacy in the world. I often ask my clients while on MDMA what they'd like to be known for by the time they die. It's a great question. Answering such a question often helps people gain clarity about what's really important– and it gives them newfound energy for pursuing such goals.

Depression as Anger Turned Inward

Depression can have various causes, from a lack of meaningful goals and feelings of loss to chemical and hormonal imbalances. Yet, many psychologists point out that depression can result from repressed, stuck, or unexpressed emotions. Like a pipe that is clogged, these emotions that aren't expressed can cause a lack of energy. According to many psychologists, the answer is to get the emotions fully expressed and flowing again. Since MDMA helps people get in touch with difficult feelings, it can be especially useful in this regard. When I guide folks who are depressed on an MDMA journey, I look to see what emotions are not being acknowledged and expressed in their lives. In many instances, it's anger. It can be anger at themselves, or anger at a mate, child, or friend, but unexpressed anger often leads to feelings of depression.

Once you know the cause of a disorder, the remedy is often apparent. When I notice a client has unexpressed anger (or some other emotion like grief), I encourage them to get in touch with it. When the main unexpressed emotion is anger, a person needs to be careful how it is vented. Anger expressed directly at other people is often counterproductive. It usually just makes the situation worse. Instead, I encourage people to express their anger the way two-year-old children do it–by yelling and hitting. Of course, you must be careful where you yell and what (not who!) you hit. To get one's anger out safely, I suggest clients turn up some music in their bedroom, then scream as they wallop their bed or a pillow with their fists until they feel exhausted. I call this doing an "adult temper tantrum." When done with enthusiasm, it should only take a couple of minutes before the unexpressed feelings are fully released.

I've found that a consistent practice of expressing anger in the manner described is quite effective in helping many people overcome depression. To make such catharsis even more effective, it helps to yell certain phrases when fully venting anger. In a highly charged state such as occurs when yelling and hitting, whatever you focus on has a major effect on your conditioning. If you yell, "People are God damn jerks," you'll likely just condition such views deeper into your psyche. Therefore, I suggest you yell a phrase that would be healthy to program into your head. I find the best phrases to encode into one's psyche are those people come up with during an MDMA session. It's as if people have an exact leak in their brains and need a specific remedy to fix it. Some of the phrases folks have come up with that feel healthy, helpful, and true for them include:

1. I'm really angry and it's okay to feel angry.

2. It's not fair, and not everything in life is fair.

3. They hurt me and I can learn to accept that.

4. I'm really sad, but this too shall pass.

5. I screwed up, but I can still accept myself.

6. I made a mistake, and I can forgive myself.

7. It's okay and safe to be angry and upset.

8. Shit happens, and I can learn to accept that.

If one of the above phrases "speaks" to you, you might give it a whirl. It's important that the phrase feel good and helpful to you since you'll want to say it repeatedly with emotional intensity. Whether you're saying such a phrase while on MDMA or when angry and hitting your bed, the combination of emotional intensity and repetition helps reprogram the brain. In fact, our prior conditioning got ingrained in us under similar circumstances when we were a kid. As a young child, when an emotionally intense or traumatic event occurred, we often developed phrases and beliefs that have stayed with us through adulthood.

Since many of the messages we picked up in childhood were unhelpful—such as "I'm not worthy of love"—we need to update the programming if we want to be happy. An MDMA journey can be like a form of mental surgery where unhelpful beliefs are rooted out and replaced with more harmonious and accurate programming. As with surgery, knowing exactly what's wrong and what is needed for health to be restored is key to a successful outcome.

Most people have negative beliefs about themselves that interfere with their feeling more joy and self-love. While they're on MDMA, I have a quick and easy way for my clients to unearth such beliefs. It's a simple form of sentence completion. I have my clients complete a specific sentence six times in a row rapidly. The sentence is, "*I can't feel joy or love myself because…*". When I recently asked a client on MDMA to do this exercise, this is what she came up with:

I can't feel joy or love myself because…

1. I'm a bad girl.
2. I don't deserve to be happy.
3. I did something wrong.
4. I need to do better.
5. I don't work hard enough.
6. I'm not good enough.

With such beliefs constantly running in her subconscious, it was hard for this high-achieving woman to ever feel joy or self-acceptance. Even though she was very successful in her career, her extra 20 pounds and constant self-judgment had her feeling depressed. In our session, she devised an "antidote" to all her negative beliefs. At first, I offered her the phrase, "I love my life and myself," but she said it didn't ring true for her. Then, she came up with the phrase, "I'm learning to feel grateful for exactly who I am." Once she said this sentence, a broad smile crossed her face. It was as if she suddenly became plugged into a light socket. During our integration session a week later, she reported that whenever she repeated her "new mantra," she felt a change in her whole demeanor and outlook. Such is the power of the right phrase to fix the leak in one's prior programming.

There are many more remedies for helping with depression than I've listed here. Along with my suggestions, things such as exercise, a good social support network, and eating and sleeping well all help immensely. The more things you try, the more likely you'll hit upon something that works well for you. In my "From Sad to Glad" program (remember, it's free), you can learn much more and get some other great techniques.

I should note that the various remedies I've described here don't work for everyone. Some folks who suffer from depression simply have a chemical imbalance in their brain or some other medical issue. That's why getting a thorough check-up from a doctor is always helpful.

However, even in such cases, the various therapeutic modalities described in this chapter can still be helpful. It's not even necessary to take MDMA to use them, although in conjunction with a guided MDMA session they tend to work much more effectively. If you suffer from depression, an MDMA session with a trained professional is definitely a good alternative. Even in cases where you are not fully "cured," the insights and skills you learn will likely make you a whole lot happier and headed in the right direction.

CHAPTER 9

USING MEDICINE FOR
SPIRITUAL DEEPENING

"MDMA allows us to experience the profound beauty and interconnectedness of the universe. It reminds us that we are all part of something greater."

— Terrence McKenna, researcher

Before diving into anything "spiritual," it's essential that we define what we're talking about. The words "spiritual" and "God" can mean very different things to different people. For example, some people view "God" as a man with a beard in the sky that often judges people and banishes them to hell for eternity if they don't do everything He suggests. (Just for the record, I'm not a fan of that view!). Other people view God very differently–such as an energy of love that permeates the universe. To clarify what I mean by "spiritual," I use that word to denote the experience of deeper love, joy, and inner peace. When I use MDMA to help people deepen their spiritual connection, I don't particularly care about their religious, spiritual, or atheistic beliefs. Instead, I aim to help them expand and deepen their daily experience of love, joy, and inner peace.

I've written several books about how to "develop" spiritually, and I have a podcast dedicated to that topic–*Awareness Explorers*. In my own pursuit of more love, joy, and inner peace, I've seen that certain beliefs and methods work extremely well for me, and some don't. When leading journeys with clients, I aim to help them ascertain what powerfully works for them. Like two detectives, we explore what beliefs, images, methods, and people help them easily tap into what has been called "the kingdom of heaven within." To my surprise, I've noticed that most people are unaware of what helps them feel more peace, love, and joy. Fortunately, once I help them become aware of easy ways to tap into uplifting feelings, their lives are never the same.

In my interviews with over 100 spiritual leaders, I have often asked, "What are human beings here to do? In other words, what's the purpose of human life?" Remarkably, virtually all these leaders have said basically the same thing. For $12.95 you can get my book, "The Enlightenment Project," and find what all of them said was the purpose of human life. I'm just kidding you. Since you bought *this* book, I'll spill the beans. According to people ranging from Deepak Chopra to the Dalai Lama, we are here to do two things: First, connect with the peace, love, and joy within ourselves and, secondly, be of service to other people and the world. Simple, but not easy. The good news is that, with the right guidance, MDMA can make our task much quicker and easier.

The Five Spiritual Love Languages

Many people have heard of the book, "The 5 Love Languages." If you aren't familiar with it, the premise of the book is that people differ in how they receive love. For example, some folks feel really loved when they are touched or have sex. Other people feel most loved when they are bought gifts, spend quality time with a lover, or hear words of appreciation. There are no "right" or "wrong" ways to express or receive love. It's just that some ways are far more compelling for a given individual. The same is true for the "5 Spiritual Love Languages."

People have different ways to tap into love, joy, and inner peace. By knowing what your tendencies are, you can more frequently tap into highly positive feelings.

In my work with my clients, I've seen there are five main approaches people have for deepening sacred feelings. Although a person might find that each of the five ways works for them to some extent, one approach usually works the best for tapping into spiritual experiences. The five approaches can briefly be described:

1. Physical= Using body positions or bodily movements to tap into more peace, love, and joy.

2. Mental= Using certain meditations, phrases, or contemplations to feel serene

3. Emotional= Using heart-expanding activities such as devotion, chanting, or service

4. Sensory= Using body sensations and bodily relaxation to dive within and be present

5. Energetic= Using awareness of subtle energies to experience deep surrender

Perhaps one of these approaches to deeper feelings of love and peace immediately strikes you as your favorite. Perhaps not. However, most people are not well acquainted with all five approaches, so they don't usually know what works best. Through experimentation and various questions I ask while they're on MDMA, my clients get a much clearer idea of what works well for them.

The Journey to Enlightenment

From books I'd read, I figured that people who claimed to be enlightened got to experience a lot of love and peace in their lives. Well, I wanted to join their club. So I asked myself, "Who on Earth knows the most about becoming enlightened?" Eventually, I came across Dr. Jeffery Martin, a Harvard-trained psychologist who had studied 1200 enlightened folks for over 20 years. Dr. Martin learned that these 1200 people used various methods that triggered expanded states of consciousness. Yet, one strategy stood out more than all the others for creating powerful and lasting results. The method was straightforward: whenever you're in an expanded state of love or peace, write about every detail of your experience you can describe.

There's a saying that "the Devil is in the details." However, it ends up that *God* is in the details, too. The most effective way to enter mystical states of love, unity, and peace is to have a written record of what and how you've entered them in the past. When I heard this, I began writing a detailed account of what I experienced on MDMA and other psychedelics. Over time, I realized that my descriptions were based on answering certain specific questions. I soon wrote down those questions, and every time I took a psychedelic or meditated my way into ecstasy, I answered these questions on paper. The 20 questions I found most helpful for learning how to access higher states of consciousness can be found below.

When I ask my clients while on MDMA these questions, they have found that their answers create a "breadcrumb trail" back to the love they felt while on the drug. Then, when they are no longer high, their specific answers help them access love (or peace or joy) much more easily than ever before. The 20 questions are:

1. What are you noticing or feeling?
2. How exactly do you experience that?
3. Exactly where do you feel that in your body? Describe to me the exact sensations you feel…and where you feel them.
4. How is your mind/inner dialogue different now than how it usually is?

5. What are you saying to yourself, or how would you describe the "lens" in which you are looking through right now?

6. Where would you say your energy in your body is currently most pronounced?

7. As you think about a person or animal you love, what do you notice in your body?

8. Can you expand the feeling of love and connection you feel even more?

9. Exactly what did you do, think, or imagine to expand the feeling of openness even more? Describe it in a way that is as precise as you can.

10. What phrase, method, or image comes to mind as a way to remind you of this experience?

11. What happens now as you use that phrase, method, or image? What do you notice?

12. Think of someone—maybe a politician or former partner who you now don't like or who has hurt you in the past. What do you notice in your body as you think of them?

13. What did you do to become more constricted or protective?

14. Can you now go back to being more open and loving?

15. What changes did you notice or what did you do to move into an open and loving direction?

16. How would you describe your experience of MDMA to someone else so that they thoroughly understand it?

17. Think of something that you have found to be upsetting. Perhaps an incident or a negative judgment about yourself. As you focus on this, what obstacles or resistance do you notice and how does that manifest?

18. Can you let go of any resistance that shows up?

19. When you attempt to let go of any resistance, what helps you to do that and/or how would you describe the experience of letting go of resistance?

20. What movement could you do, or what songs do you know that might help you to remember this experience when you are not on the medicine?

As you probably noticed in reading these 20 questions, they all point to very precise aspects of one's direct experience. Some questions even point to how a person blocks or avoids being open to uplifting feelings. The reason why I ask such questions is for two reasons. First, if you want to stay open, you need to know the first signs that you're closing down—so you don't necessarily close down completely. Secondly, sometimes you want to be able to curtail your level of openness. Different situations call for varying levels of openness to love and other people's energies. If you're fully open and vulnerable in stressful environments or with people with bad energy, you'll suffer more than is necessary. By being able to curtail your level of openness, you can be less affected and less drained by challenging people and situations.

I often give my clients a helpful analogy to explain the potential value of learning how to open and close their "heart energy field." I tell them that a hand is "handy" because it can open and close at will. If your hand could only stay open, it would be more like a fly swatter. On the other hand, if it could only remain closed (like a fist), it would be like a club. Neither would be very useful. But because a hand can quickly open or close to fit what's needed in the moment, it's an incredibly useful instrument. Likewise, a person that can quickly open their heart or close it down for protection when necessary is best able to adapt to whatever is appropriate and needed.

Recently, I recorded a client's transcript on MDMA as I asked her some questions about her experience. While the 20 listed questions can certainly help ascertain beneficial information, I mostly just follow my curiosity. I am trying to learn exactly how they create, expand, and curtail their expanded state of love, joy, and peace. This is an edited version of how this exploration went with my client, Sarah:

> **JR:** You look like you're feeling pretty high. On a 1 to 10 scale, with 10 being you feel more love and joy than you've ever felt, and 1 being you feel anxious and uncomfortable, what number would you give yourself right now?
>
> **Sarah**: I'd say a 7 and a half. I'm feeling really good.
>
> **JR:** Great. Now I'd like to do a few short, guided meditations with you and hopefully we'll learn some key information as to how you create this really good feeling. I want to begin by having you focus on a person or beloved pet that you really love. Imagine wonderful times with this being…If you want, you can imagine hugging them or holding them so you feel even more connected. (long pause). Allow yourself to feel gratitude for their being in your life…Now, on the 1 to 10 scale, how do you feel.
>
> **Sarah**: A ten! I don't want to ever leave this experience…
>
> **JR:** Fantastic…Now I'm wondering what changed internally when you went from 7.5 to a ten? Was there an energy or some other shift in your body? If so, how did that manifest?
>
> **Sarah**: I noticed I sat up straighter to better align with a wave of energy moving up my spine. Also, it feels like my heart got bigger, or like there are rays of energy shooting out from it.
>
> **JR:** Sounds wonderful! Is there a phrase or image or song that perhaps goes along with this amazing feeling?

Sarah: (long pause). Yes, there's a Christian song where the chorus is simply, "Whoa, I praise your Name…" That began playing in my head. The image is my heart throbbing and throwing off beams of light.

JR: That's great. Now you know some simple ways to perhaps tap into that love and joy more easily when you're not on this medicine. Just a couple more questions. Can you think of a time when you were greatly challenged–perhaps mad at or really upset with someone? Focus on that situation and time as best you can…

Sarah: (long pause). Okay, I remember.

JR: What did you notice in your body as you remembered this unpleasant experience? Did you feel a constriction somewhere? Did something else happen?

Sarah: I felt something like a shield of energy tighten around my chest–like I'm getting ready to move into a fetal position. I noticed my eyes looking down and my shoulders slumped.

JR: Great. That's useful information. If you ever feel a need to shield or protect yourself, now you know how you naturally do that. Where are you on that 1 to 10 scale now?

Sarah: Probably a 4.

JR: Would you like to move up that scale again?

Sarah: Yes please.

JR: Well, you know the recipe for how to do that…You can focus on someone you love…then sit up straight; feel the center of your chest with your heart radiating beams of light…

Sarah: Oh, yes! This feels great…

JR: Now allow yourself to sing that song you love inside your head. Imagine singing it directly to God. (long pause). What number would you give yourself now?

Sarah: An Eleven!

JR: That's super. Now you have a recipe or breadcrumb trail back to this expansive feeling of love. Congratulations. So now, I have a very different question for you: What do you think is typically in the way of this expansive love you're feeling?

Sarah: I'm often thinking I should be doing something else, like getting something important done.

JR: Good…as you now think of getting something done, or the need to get something done, what do you notice in your body?

Sarah: It's as if I leave this bathtub of love I'm in and I enter a whole other energy of buzzing bees inside my body. It feels chaotic, especially around my chest.

JR: That's a good observation. Can you soften those "buzzing bees" by using the heart image, or the praising phrase, or some other way to soften back into the love energy?

Sarah: Yes, yes, that feels so much better. Wow, that was quick…

JR: Great. You're learning to easily relax back into your true nature of love. Nothing is more important than that…

As you read in this transcript, taking a client (or yourself) through this process can yield valuable information. I liken this procedure to a camera taking a clear picture of an event. Most people only have the fuzziest notion of how their mind and body open–or curtail–the experience of love. This love "training" process helps add much more clarity and detail to the picture. Then, when a person is not on MDMA, it's a lot easier for them to get back to open-heartedness because they now know what they unconsciously do to get there. With a little practice, they can often enter higher states of consciousness much more quickly than before.

You may have noticed that I often asked my client what number she was on a 1 to 10 scale. Having a "scale" that rates the intensity of her experience of love is helpful in a couple of ways. First, it helps me track what she is experiencing. I can best guide my clients if I accurately know what is happening with them. Second, it allows me to do different "experiments" with her to see what helps her to "open" or "close." As I suggest various ways she can enter more deeply into love and joy, she can immediately see what worked, and what had little effect. Having an internal rating scale allows a person to learn things about their subjective experience that normally are hard to ascertain.

When I used this process on myself, I learned over 25 specific things I did to open or close down my heart energy field. It was fun and fascinating to discover phrases, body movements, images, songs, and precise methods that quickly led me to ecstatic bliss. I felt like a spiritual Sherlock Holmes looking for subtle clues that would help me find more love inside myself. Once I went through this process, I took the best nuggets of my observations and wrote them all down on a 3" X 5" card. Then, I had the card laminated. Nowadays, each morning I use one or more of the many suggestions on the card to quickly enter into deep feelings of love, joy, and peace. In addition, I often take two-minute breaks throughout the day to tap into these higher states of consciousness. It's my absolute favorite thing to do!

Deepening into love—and even learning ways we avoid such feelings—is important spiritual work. Rather than getting lost in unhelpful beliefs or practices that provide no real peace, this exploratory process can give a person truly helpful information. Socrates said it's important to "know thyself." By knowing exactly how we open our hearts—and block such experiences—we can bring more love, joy, and peace into our daily lives.

CHAPTER 10

DOING X ON YOUR OWN

"MDMA is not a party drug; it's a catalyst for introspection and self-discovery. It can help us confront our fears and heal our wounds."

— Daniel Pinchbeck, author

First, a warning. Doing MDMA therapy on yourself is not as easy as it may first seem. Of course, there are legal and safety concerns as stated before in this book, but in addition, self-guided therapy can be challenging when difficult issues arise. Seeking professional guidance for addressing inner wounds is far safer than attempting self-guided therapy. On the other hand, MDMA can help open you up to more self-love than you may have ever felt. Nevertheless, it should be stated that working on one's inner wounds on a self-guided journey is especially hard. When you're high and floating in cosmic bliss, following any intention you may have brought into the session is challenging. Yet, therapy is an intentional undertaking. When having an intention, by definition, you're trying to accomplish something. Therefore, if you want to do MDMA therapy on your own, you'll need to carefully prepare things before your journey to increase the likelihood of success.

Another reason "solo journeys" have limitations is that most of our wounds in life happen in a relational context. We mostly experience trauma, anxiety, and even depression in relation to what others do to us–or don't do to us. Such wounds can certainly be explored by oneself, but the most significant healing happens when they arise within a trusting relationship. Indeed, one of the reasons why self-help books don't usually lead to healing is because there's no actual relationship with the author. Unfortunately, increased information and awareness of a problem rarely lead to actual transformation.

…All that said, you can still get valuable insights from a solo journey if you set things up well. When someone tells me they want to do a self-guided journey, I ask them a few questions to see if they are adequately prepared. Here are a few of the questions I like to ask:

1. Did you experience trauma growing up and have you ever had trauma-type reactions come up on previous psychedelic trips?

2. Are you in a good mental space for doing a solo journey, or are you trying to escape from some feelings?

3. Do you know what size dose would best serve your intention, and are you careful about not taking too much?

4. Are you able to create an environment that supports whatever intention you have?

As these questions indicate, there are many things you can do to prepare for a self-guided MDMA therapy session. The first among these is to have a mate or friend "on call" in case you feel the need for support or help of any kind. I always ask my wife or a friend to be available during a self-guided trip in case something comes up that is challenging for me. Second, it's important to be clear about what you hope to explore or accomplish during your self-guided journey. I suggest journaling about your intention rather than just thinking about it. When we write something in a journal or into a document on our computer, it makes it more real to us than just thinking about it. In addition, when an intention is written down, it's easier to access when you're in an altered state. This lesson took me a while to learn. In my early days of exploration, there were many times I had thought of an intention for a journey, but once the drug took effect, I couldn't remember what the heck the intention was. Don't let this happen to you.

Another common mistake is to have too many intentions or have your purpose be rather vague. If you want to create more than one intention for a journey, rank them in order of importance. Of course, once you're high, you may realize that a new order of priority is what is called for. Alternatively, you may find the medicine triggers something you hadn't thought of before. Therefore, your list of intentions needs to be held lightly, and if something you hadn't thought of before shows up, it's generally best to go with what feels the "juiciest" to you.

There are many kinds of intentions I've brought into my MDMA journeys. What follows are ten specific aims I've focused on while on MDMA. As you'll read in the following section, each intention is in the form of a question I'm trying to investigate and receive answers to more fully. Each question aims to explore how to create a life of more peace, love, and effectiveness in the world. With the help of MDMA, the answers I have received to these questions have added a tremendous amount of depth, insight, and practical value to my life. I hope they are equally valuable to you.

When focusing on any of these questions, I first center myself by focusing on my breath. Then, I look at the question in my journal and repeat it quietly to let it sink in. Soon, multiple insights bubble up all at once. As the insights arise, I write them down in my journal. Sometimes new questions bubble up as my initial insights are written down. If strong feelings come up related to the topic at hand, I try to follow that feeling until new insights or memories arise.

To help you get the most value from these questions, after each one is listed, I'll explain why they could be so beneficial to explore while on MDMA.

The Self-Therapy Questions

1. What do I need to know to move forward in my life or career?
I love this question. When I've asked it, the answers have often surprised me. Sometimes I have intuited that I should write a new book—including this one! Other times information about friendships, finances, or health issues have arisen. I feel like MDMA helps me get in touch with my intuition. Sometimes my "intuition" feels like a "still, small voice" or just a strong feeling of what I need to do. Occasionally I've even received pictures in my head that suggested what I needed to know or do. Perhaps the most common way my intuition "talks" to me is through my body. If I ask my intuition a "yes" or "no" question, my body responds very differently to when I feel a "yes" than when I feel a "no." However you receive intuitive guidance, asking how to move forward in your life will likely spark useful information that can improve your life.

2. How can I open to more love in my life?
Love is perhaps the most important thing in life. One of the times I was on *The Oprah Show* was with a panel of people who had died for a short period of time, then were brought back to life—what's called a "near-death experience." I found it fascinating that everyone said that when they reviewed their life, they felt they were being asked a single question. It was the same question for everyone: "What have you learned about love?" If that's the "lens" through which we review our lives when we die, we may as well prepare for the final exam of life right now! By asking this question and listening for any intuitive answer you receive, you're exploring what's fundamental to why we are here on Earth.

3. What gets in the way of loving myself?

On my podcast, *Awareness Explorers,* I often ask the various enlightened teachers I interview, "What was key to you becoming a highly awake being?" The number one answer I've received in over 100 interviews is "learning to love and fully accept myself, especially the parts of me that seemed unlovable." Many of these teachers say that love is our true nature, so to love yourself, you need only see what's in the way. Seeing the obstacles to self-love can help reveal subtle ways we reject or constrict ourselves. Once you see such impediments more clearly, they naturally dissolve over time.

4. What blocks me from deeper intimacy with my mate?

If you're like me, you probably crave moments of deep connection and intimacy with whoever you're in a relationship with. However, if you're like me, you may find yourself avoiding such intimate moments. So why don't those moments happen more often? Sincerely asking this question will often reveal little things you and I do that interfere with vulnerability and deep connection. Fortunately, one clue for finding greater intimacy is hidden in the word: in to me see. When we divulge vulnerable details about ourselves, intimacy grows. When I've asked this question to myself, I've often seen how I use humor, blame, and busyness to avoid intimacy. Perhaps as you ask yourself this question, you'll become aware of such behaviors as well. Awareness is always the first step in having any undesirable behavior change.

5. Who do I need to forgive? Can I forgive them?

Many religions and spiritual teachers talk about the importance of forgiveness. When we fail to forgive others—or ourselves—it's like walking around with a backpack full of rocks on our shoulders. A lack of forgiveness is a burden. This question about forgiveness can help you know if you're still carrying those rocks around, and if so, prompt you to let them go. How? Actually, it's easy. When you notice that carrying around a closed heart (or a backpack of rocks) feels heavy, you simply decide to let it go. Ultimately, forgiveness is an act of self-love.

6. Is there anything I have withheld saying to someone that would be beneficial to express?

When people think about the biggest regrets in their life, topping the list is often something about not expressing their true feelings to others. These unexpressed feelings can be of a positive or negative nature. Either way, unexpressed feelings tend to zap us of peace and happiness. For example, when you fail to tell the people you love that you *do* love them, you miss moments of potential connection. When you avoid saying when you're hurt or upset at someone, those feelings stay stuck in you. This question in which you're exploring "withholds" is a simple way to make sure you free yourself from emotional blockages.

7. Why do I get so triggered when (fill in the blank) happens or (X person) does (fill in the blank)?

I put this question in generic form, with a couple of blanks for you to fill in as it applies to you. For example, I recently asked myself: "Why do I get so triggered when I get bad service at a restaurant, and the waiter doesn't quickly take my order?" We all have things that trigger us in ways that make a mountain out of a molehill. For me, it's lousy service. When I explored this topic while on MDMA, I remembered many times my parents failed to give me the attention I craved when I was a child—and how abandoned I felt. When I realized my current upsets were related to my childhood events, it took the edge off of them. As you explore events or people that trigger you, the insights gained can make a major difference in healing those wounds.

8. What part(s) in me get in the way of deeper peace?

In previous sections of this book, I've briefly mentioned the modality known as IFS or Internal Family Systems. In that system, people are posited to be made up of many subpersonalities. This question about "parts" looks to see if any subpersonality is causing unexpressed trouble or interfering with peace. I have found that, while on MDMA, I have often been able to dialog with a part of me that needs special attention. Inevitably, when I listen to the part that needs attention or feels abandoned, a deep feeling of peace results. If this type of work interests you, get the book "Self-Therapy" by Jay Early so you can learn to work and dialog with your various parts.

9. How would my life or behavior differ if I had no fear of failure or disapproval?

If you're honest with yourself, you probably know that the fear of failure or others' opinions has a massive impact on your life. This question helps to clarify what freedom from those concerns would look like. I've found that when I've asked this while on MDMA, I get a clearer vision of who I want to be, as well as behaviors and beliefs that are obstacles to my ideal self. As I've said before, you're halfway to your target once you know what keeps you from a goal.

10. If I could change one thing about myself or my life now, what would it be?

This question allows me to focus on the one thing that, if it were improved, would make a big difference in my life. This question has a lot of practical value. Often, there are many things we would like to be different about ourselves or our life. Yet, change is hard, so it's best to focus on just one thing at a time. When I've received a clear answer to this question, it has helped me to focus my energies so that clear progress can be made. By asking yourself this question, usually one particular thing will stand out to you.

I don't pretend to have a monopoly on good questions and helpful intentions. If one or more of these questions speak to you, use them. If not, create your own intentions and questions that excite you or seem of practical value. Whatever questions you ask, your level of sincerity in really wanting to know the answer is key to receiving great insight. Fortunately, MDMA makes listening to one's deeper intuition much easier and more likely than usual.

Another helpful aspect of MDMA is the fact that it gives most people better access to their feelings from the past. If something is troubling me, on MDMA I can fearlessly dive into that feeling and see what arises. Sometimes it's a new insight about a relationship with a friend or a new perspective on a challenging situation. Yet, perhaps the most interesting things that arise are when I focus on a feeling and that feeling brings up memories of my early childhood. Sometimes I'll even ask myself, "When can I remember first feeling this?" Inevitably, memories arise, and sometimes those recollections are of events that were quite unpleasant. However, the fact that I'm on MDMA and feel totally safe helps me reprocess or "digest" those memories in a loving or neutralizing way.

On rare occasions, a self-therapy MDMA session will bring up a big issue that you were not previously aware of. When that happens, it's best to seek the help of a qualified therapist for further exploration and assistance. In addition, in case you experience a prolonged rough spot, having a friend or mate nearby can reassure you or be there for you to make your journey easier.

During one solo MDMA trip I did, it brought up a profound memory from my past that I had forgotten—but had clearly shaped my life. When I was five years old, my dad took me to a Beatles concert. Back in 1965, Beatlemania was in full swing. It was total mayhem. As a five-year-old, I had confused the Beatles with God. Therefore, I had a profound spiritual experience at the concert. The fact that I was clearly the youngest person at the concert made me feel incredibly special. After all, I was the youngest person getting to witness "God" in human form—or so I thought. Later in my life, I felt practically entitled to be able to interview and spend time with people such as the Dalai Lama or various gurus. People often asked me why I felt qualified to get to know such esteemed teachers. I realized it traced back to this time with my dad when I got to see the "four body God" as a young child. It made me feel especially close and grateful to my dad for how his kindness shaped my life.

Non-Therapy Therapy

Sometimes the best insights come to a person when they're not searching for insights. We've all heard of people who have worked on a problem for days with no result. Then, the answer magically appears once they relax by going for a walk or taking a bath. Well, the same thing can happen on MDMA. The MAPS protocol for working with people on MDMA depends mainly on this approach. Patients are instructed to simply listen to evocative music with a blindfold on. Amazingly, important insights and healing of PTSD symptoms are the frequent results. Therefore, it's worth giving this indirect form of therapy a try. All you need to do is create a playlist with some of your favorite music. It's important that some of the music you choose not have lyrics to them so your mind is less engaged. If you try this approach, I suggest having a journal or smartphone nearby so you can record your best insights.

Besides listening to music with a blindfold on, taking time in nature can also be healing. Of course, don't drive while under the influence of the drug, but taking a walk should be no problem. Many people who take MDMA and spend time in nature have a newfound appreciation for the outdoors. I once spent an entire afternoon watching birds while on MDMA. Ever since that experience, I greatly enjoy watching birds. Strangely, it wasn't until my experience of watching birds while high on MDMA that I could truly appreciate what amazing creatures birds are.

Another form of indirect therapy is to read from Holy books or any book that inspires you. Nowadays, we're all so busy that we often don't take time to sit down and really absorb the wisdom of what we read.

(Hopefully, you're absorbing what you're reading now!). But a good book can be like a trusted friend, allowing you to feel your deep inner knowing and wisdom. As I've read from certain books while on MDMA, the insights have often "hit" me in ways that had lasting impact. Therefore, I usually have a couple of books by my side when I take MDMA alone just in case reading from them feels right.

The various "non-therapy therapies" I just discussed can serve another purpose. Listening to music, being with nature, and reading from revered books can create a sacred space for your journey. When doing MDMA on your own, initiating a beneficial set and setting is fully up to you. I suggest creating a ritual before taking the medicine that speaks to your heart and spirit. Since everyone is different, the ritual you create should be whatever helps you go deep within. Besides music, nature, and readings, you may find that a heartfelt prayer, a dance, or invoking a chosen spiritual guide can help get you ready for your sacred journey. Ultimately, what you get from an MDMA session done on your own is equal to the sincerity and effort you put into it.

In this chapter, I've provided many suggestions for how to use MDMA for self-therapy without the help of a guide. Take the tips that seemed useful to you and leave the rest. Part of the value of doing a session alone is exploring what "calls" to you while in a higher state of consciousness. MDMA is a great way to get to know yourself in a deeper way than usual. If done with a clear intention, it can be a form of self-love, and most of us can really use some more nurturance and love in our lives.

CHAPTER 11

COMMUNICATION MIRACLES
FOR COUPLES

"...The connectedness, actual real connectedness, not the fake bullshit connectedness that you get when you're twatting about. On MDMA, it's like genuine telepathy or something, isn't it?"

— Stefan Mohamed, author

In 1997, I wrote a book called *Communication Miracles for Couples.* It ended up becoming a *New York Times* bestseller. Soon, I was inundated with couples wanting to do counseling with me. With practice, I got pretty good at it. Yet occasionally, I would encounter a couple in such bad shape that nothing I tried would work with them. A married couple, I'll call them Martha and Joe, had been arguing in my office for over a year of weekly sessions. Finally, in a desperate attempt to help them, I suggested they take Ecstasy together while I guided them to repair their relationship. Since the only alternative was a nasty divorce and custody battle, they were willing to try.

I enjoy doing couples counseling because you don't have to wonder what their underlying problem is. Typically, couples are more than happy to demonstrate their lousy relationship habits in the office. Of all the patterns that get couples in trouble, #1, #2, and #3 are blaming, shaming, and complaining. Somehow, dysfunctional couples all believe that if they could prove their partner is terribly wrong, all would change and be harmonious. It's as if they hope to hear from their partner the following words: "Yes, *now* I see what you've been blaming me for, and it's all true! I'm *so* sorry I've been acting that way. *Thank you* for showing me the errors of my ways! I will need to change immediately!" Of course, such words have never been sincerely spoken on this planet. All efforts at blaming, shaming, and complaining are wasted energy and only serve to make things worse.

With Martha and Joe, they were so used to yelling at each other that I wasn't sure if the MDMA would help. However, I'd had luck with plenty of couples before them, so I was hopeful. Once the drug began taking effect, their whole demeanor changed. I had never seen that Martha and Joe even *liked* each other–much less love each other. While they had initially sat on opposite sides of my couch, now they were holding hands and looking into each other's eyes. Then, they spontaneously began listing all the things they loved about each other. Without my help, they started apologizing for everything they had said and done to each other. By now, all three of us were in tears. Finally, I suggested we go over the many issues they had (previously) had with each other. To my amazement, they rationally and lovingly agreed on all their relevant issues. I had witnessed a true communication miracle.

I'm not saying that MDMA alone can magically solve all issues between couples–although sometimes that does indeed happen. Nevertheless, this medicine and a good therapist can do wonders. It can create a feeling of deep connection that has often been lacking between two people. Working out challenging issues with someone you don't trust and are mad at is practically impossible. Fortunately, working out problems with someone you love and respect is relatively easy. The positive feelings MDMA helps create allow couples to work out issues in one afternoon that might have taken years of therapy to produce.

A common question I get about working with couples on MDMA is, "Do the positive feelings and solutions they arrive at really last?" The answer is "yes, no, and it depends." I tell couples that any agreements they make while on the medicine will not be valid until they are confirmed by each person in an integration session. My reassurance makes it easier for couples to work out agreeable solutions while on the drug. Later, during their integration session about a week later, I find that couples almost always find the agreements they made while on MDMA still work for them.

Since my clients record the sessions on their smartphone, couples get to hear what it was like when they felt fully connected to each other. This often brings up a yearning to return to that loving place again. We all know it's better to be connected in our hearts than battling it out in our heads, but the recordings drive home the point. Hearing words of love and understanding from their partner on the recording often gives them new hope that they can turn things around. In the integration session, I explain that their MDMA journey was just the beginning and that new communication habits must be established. However, because they experienced a new possibility during their session, couples can often make much better use of future counseling together.

One of the advantages of couples' therapy with MDMA is how quickly it helps them better understand each other. People yearn to be understood, and most couples are not very good at understanding their partners. I never have a couple come to my office and say, "We really understand each other very well–that's why we want a divorce." On the other hand, couples will often say in exasperated tones, "They just don't understand me–*that's* why I want a divorce." If I can help two people really grasp their partner's feelings and viewpoint, and empathize with their experience, magic happens. MDMA makes that job a whole lot easier.

A Healing Flow

The first step in MDMA-assisted therapy for couples is to do a "discovery" call. Typically, that involves a one-hour Zoom call to ascertain if this type of work is right for them, and to talk about their goals for a journey together. If we're all in agreement, we schedule a five-hour time in which to do the session. In most cases, the couple ingests the medicine thirty minutes before we're all on Zoom together. I begin the session by seeing how they're doing and answering any questions. Depending on the couple's background and desires, we may create a sacred space by my leading a guided meditation, saying a prayer, or listening to a favorite song.

My experience guiding many couples has led to developing a typical structure for how a successful session unfolds. Of course, I always follow the medicine and the couple's needs, but I've seen there tends to be an optimal order for things to happen that lead to maximal healing. During the first part of the journey, I have the couple connect emotionally. Once the couple can feel the medicine, their defenses usually evaporate, and they can again fall in love. At that point, I'll often suggest they play *The Appreciation Game.* In this "game," partners take turns saying something they appreciate or love about each other. This activity is both heartwarming to watch and often leads to even deeper feelings of love and connection.

Once a couple is basking in good feelings, I often suggest they play *The Curiosity Game.* In this activity, each person takes turns asking any question they're curious about or don't understand about their partner. Some of these questions can be pretty edgy, such as, "Why did you have an affair?" or "Why don't you ever want to make love anymore?" Usually, in daily life couples don't ask such questions or talk honestly about these challenging subjects. In fact, it can often turn into a catastrophe if they try to bring up such issues. However, the more couples understand and are honest with each other, the more they can work through their problems.

When on MDMA, as couples share their questions and answers with each other, if things go off course, I steer things back on course.

Once couples have created more understanding between each other, I'll sometimes guide them a step deeper. That often involves couples sharing regrets and apologizing for hurtful past behavior. I help the couple "clear the air" of past wrongs so they can better express what they each want in the future. I'll often have partners take turns completing the following sentence five times:

"In the future, what I'd like in our relationship is (fill in the blank)…"

Couples normally tell each other what they *don't* want, leading to more distance between them. When I can get two people to vulnerably communicate what they *do* want, new dynamics suddenly become possible.

After each partner states several things they want to create or do with their mate, we move on to trying to work through past issues. Working on issues while people feel burdened by the past or not fully connected is a losing game. That's why the healing process between two people must occur in a particular order. But, like with all journey work, I hold my agenda and ideas about timing very lightly. Each session and each moment while guiding a journey requires a deep appreciation for what is organically unfolding.

At a time that I feel working through issues is appropriate, I'll ask each partner what they feel needs to change in their relationship. I'm regularly amazed that their prior habit of blaming, shaming, and complaining is completely absent. Instead, I hear rational and loving discussions as to what they each need to do differently. Normally, it can take months or years of therapy before a couple can have a sensible and practical discussion such as this. Fortunately, the MDMA medicine does most of the "work," and I just make suggestions if I feel they're needed. It's wonderful to witness two people lovingly and honestly discussing their issues without blame or animosity.

If a couple feels stuck about what to do about an issue, I'll sometimes make suggestions. In the case of Martha and Joe, they had spent a year in my office and many years beforehand arguing about money. Martha thought Joe was "a cheap bastard," and Joe thought Martha was "an indulgent princess." They never could agree how to spend money, or who should have control over it. According to them, they had argued about money for "ten hours a week for the last twenty years."

While *The Curiosity Game* had given each of them more insight and understanding of the other's position, they still needed to agree on how to handle money moving forward. At this point, I suggested they explore what I call *The Problem-Solving Question*. *The Problem-Solving Question* simply involves asking one's partner, "What are a couple of ideas you have for handling this issue that might work better for both of us?" Then, you listen for at least two ideas your partner has for handling a particular problem. Once they state their possible solutions, you offer two potential solutions of your own. Then, you negotiate something tolerable for both of you.

Couples usually spend most of their time blaming their partner for the issues at hand—which is a waste of time and energy. Instead, *The Problem-Solving Question* gets a couple to generate multiple solutions, then negotiate to something they both are willing to try. Blaming can continue forever, but most negotiations only last a few minutes. I tell my clients they can always renegotiate any agreements they settle on. In fact, I suggest that any agreements are only good until our integration session a week later. The short time span makes it easier for couples to try a potential solution—even if they think it's not ideal. In the case of Martha and Joe, they both reluctantly agreed that Joe would give her $300 to spend any way she wanted for the next week. Neither liked the agreement, but they both could live with it for one week.

A week later, I saw Joe and Martha for our integration session. I barely recognized them. The way they were looking at each other made them look like newlyweds. I asked them, "So, what was your week like, and how did your money agreement work out for each of you?" To my surprise, they both said, "Wonderful," simultaneously. Joe went on to state, "This was the first week in maybe twenty years we didn't argue about money. It was amazing. That gave us the time and energy to love each other. We had more sex this week than in the last two years." Martha seemed equally pleased.

I asked them if they wanted to keep the money agreement they made while on MDMA. Amusingly, they each complained that they didn't think the agreement was fair. Martha said, "He's still being cheap, but it's better than arguing all the time."

Joe stated, "I don't know how she can spend so much money, but it's worth every penny not to have to discuss it anymore." I congratulated both for realizing that enjoying the fragrance of love is more important than being right or getting everything they want. Amazingly, they had solved their decades-long issue in a single day of connection, guidance, and medicine.

The Two Needed Skills

In my work with couples, I've seen there are two skills every couple needs to maintain a loving relationship. Of course, we're never taught these skills, so many relationships soon crash and burn. In an ideal world, we'd learn in school some practical ways to connect and solve problems with each other instead of spending years going over geometry and algebra equations. Unfortunately, we don't live in an ideal world, so most couples spend a lot of time arguing or feeling separate.

As I previously mentioned, one of the skills couples could benefit from is problem-solving. *The Problem-Solving Question* is a technique to help couples generate multiple solutions, then negotiate to an agreed-upon course of action. It sounds simple, but I've noticed that another skill is often needed even *before* that question can be asked. It's the ability to acknowledge the reality and feelings of one's partner. This is surprisingly hard to do when not on MDMA, and incredibly easy to do while on the medicine.

Before Martha and Joe's MDMA session, I tried to help them learn to acknowledge each other's experiences and emotions. I even gave them a shorthand way of doing this, which I call *The Acknowledgment Formula*. I told them, "When your partner talks about any subject that's important to them, in your response, fill in the following two sentences:"

"It sounds like…" (summarize what they said in one sentence or less)
"That must feel…" (guess as to how they felt about that)

Prior to Martha and Joe taking MDMA, this is how they communicated:

> **Martha:** I feel like I never have any power in this relationship. You hold all the purse strings and use them to control and manipulate me all the time. It's totally unfair.

> **Joe:** That's totally not true. I'm having to keep watch on you and not give you your own credit card so you don't go off the rails and continually buy every stupid nick-nack you can stuff into the house.

> **Martha:** You don't even hear anything I'm saying. You're basically a cheap bastard and you don't want to admit it.

…You get the picture. This would go on and on until everyone (including me) was ready to scream. Now, when the same subject of money came up while they were on MDMA, they were able to use The Acknowledgment Formula to have a very different conversation and outcome. Here's what transpired while on MDMA:

> **Martha:** I haven't felt like I have much power in our relationship, especially when it comes to money. You won't even let

me have a credit card. It's embarrassing, and I get resentful. That's been really hard.

Joe: It sounds like…you feel disempowered by my way of handling money. That must feel very hurtful and frustrating.

Martha: Yes! You get it! Thank you for understanding my experience. That feels so wonderful!

…As you can see from these short samples, a little bit of good communication can go a long way to helping each partner feel understood. I've found that once each partner feels understood, solving problems is relatively easy. On the other hand, solving a problem before each partner feels their view is acknowledged and understood is practically impossible.

The Integration Session

During the integration session with couples, I first ask them how their week has gone and what it was like to listen to the recording. In most cases, they've had a very good week–but not always. Sometimes the gap between their usual way of relating and the love expressed on the recording can stir up intense sadness or frustration. I acknowledge those feelings and suggest that such emotions are part of the road to recovery. Then, I remind couples of some of the key insights from the session, and any agreements they made while on the medicine.

Next, we discuss whether they want to keep those agreements, change them, or simply "play it by ear." During this discussion, I prompt them to use their new communication technique–*The Acknowledgment Formula*. Things tend to go very well to the extent that they can do that. By the end of the session, I give couples a vision of how they can move forward lovingly. I often suggest they continue with counseling sessions periodically to ensure they don't fall back into old patterns. It's quite satisfying to see couples go from acute animosity–to being amiable and agreeable–in a few short hours of work.

As the title of this book suggests, Ecstasy *is* medicine. It's medicine for the heart, the soul and for a couple's connection. When two people can reconnect in the exquisite euphoria of unconditional love, any problem can be solved. By using MDMA with a trusted guide or therapist, most couples can repair past hurts and return to a place of love in an amazingly short time.

PART III

FROM INSIGHTS TO IN LIFE

In the final section of this book, I reveal how to take the insights and perspectives of an MDMA journey and get them to impact your day-to-day life. To accomplish this integration work, it helps to discuss topics ranging from motivation and identity to the new ways MDMA and other substances can be used for therapy.

MY LIFE HAS BEEN ENRICHED WITH MANY WONDERFUL INSIGHTS,

WHICH I HAVE NOW ENTIRELY FORGOTTEN.

Ashleigh Brilliant

CHAPTER 12

MOTIVATION, IDENTITY, AND INTEGRATION

"MDMA makes you feel like everything is perfect and beautiful, but it's just a glimpse. It shows you what's possible, but it's up to you to integrate that into your life."

— Amber Lyon, author

There's a famous saying that we're only as strong as our weakest link. Very true. Suppose you are a billionaire, young, attractive, and intelligent, but you have a terrible toothache. In that case, the quality of your life is affected by your toothache much more than all your good fortune. In therapy, the weakest link almost always involves integration and follow-through. Awareness of what a problem is does not necessarily help with its healing. What's needed to truly transform a person's life over time are four ingredients:

1. Awareness as to what the real issues are.

2. A vision or hope that transformation is indeed possible.

3. An effective method to help with a person's difficulties.

4. A practical method to consistently motivate a person to do what helps.

Whenever any one of these four ingredients is lacking, little or no transformation occurs. In my experience, people often have an awareness of what their issues are. However, a new vision for themselves, a good method to change, and a way to stay motivated are usually sorely deficient. In this chapter, I'll discuss how to help someone develop a new vision for themselves of what's possible and some ideas for staying motivated long term. Then, in the next chapter, I'll reveal some amazing techniques for ensuring you or your clients use those methods.

Whether a person is trying to make a lot of money, heal from trauma, have a good relationship, or lose weight, there are only two steps to success. First, find out what ideas or methods work to succeed in that domain. Second, be *consistent* with that approach or method for an extended period of time. Once again, people often know what to do. That's usually not the problem. Everyone wanting to lose weight knows they should eat less (and nutritiously) or exercise more. No mystery there. But few people can do what they know for an extended timeframe. One reason for that is that they have an identity locked in the past. If you think of yourself as poor and fat, you won't be able to do the things that would make you rich and fit.

To truly elicit a transformation that "sticks," it helps to change someone's identity or self-image so they can, at the very least, *imagine* being a new type of person. Frequently, clients have spent 20, 30, or even 50 years with the identity of being a powerless victim. They may have a great MDMA session, but to heal and move forward with their lives, their identity needs to shift–or not much changes. So, the question is, "How can you change someone's self-image enough that they're inspired to consistently do what they need to move forward?" Great question. I'm glad you asked ☺

Changing a Stuck Identity

There are many methods for helping people change their beliefs about themselves and what's possible. As with anything, different things work for different people. If you're an MDMA guide, your job is to make an educated guess as to what techniques or ideas will be most helpful for your client. If you're working on yourself, your job is to listen to your intuition. When trying to change your beliefs and self-image, you can know what sounds good to you and what does not. In this section, I'll present various ideas and methods, and your task is to listen to yourself and notice what feels exciting or most helpful to try.

In college, I was the head of the hypnosis lab at UC Santa Barbara. I was amazed that I could sometimes completely change a person's identity in five minutes. Occasionally, I would do shows at fraternities where I would hypnotize some shy, nerdy guy to think he was Mick Jagger. Amazingly, some guys who were so shy they could barely speak would jump up on a table and start belting away, "I can't get nooooo... satisfaction!" That's quite an identity shift in a short time. From such experiences, I realized that hypnosis can be a quick way to shift the identity of some people. However, hypnosis doesn't work for everyone. Only about 25% of folks make really good hypnotic subjects. If you've ever talked or walked in your sleep, or you frequently remember your dreams, you're likely to be one of those people who can be easily hypnotized. If so, I suggest you research that avenue.

If hypnosis is not your thing, there are many other approaches to opening the human mind to new possibilities. As Michael Pollan's excellent book, "How to Change Your Mind," makes clear, many psychedelics can help people open to new ways of seeing themselves. When people have intense experiences–good or bad–it affects their self-image. On countless occasions, I've seen people who didn't think of themselves as "spiritual" have their identity shift as they floated in clouds of divine love while on MDMA. Once they had that singular experience, they could imagine new possibilities for their future. So, adventuring into new and intense experiences is another practical approach for shifting someone's identity.

In my life, I always thought of myself as very intellectual, but not very heart oriented. Yet, as I grew older, I recognized that most of the "goodies" in life came from feeling love, joy, and an open heart. So, I sought out intense experiences that might shift how I thought of myself. I spent time with devotion-oriented gurus, chanted divine love songs, and frequently watched movies with love stories that made me cry. At first, many of these activities felt like an uncomfortable stretch. Yet soon, I felt hopeful that I could become much more than a head with legs. That kept me motivated to consistently pursue practices that helped to open my heart. Nowadays, I haven't lost my intellect, but people tell me I'm now very heart oriented–and I feel that way internally too. It feels wonderful.

Besides pursuing psychedelic or other intense experiences, who you hang out with has a powerful impact on how you see yourself and your future. Countless studies have shown that if you want to be rich, hang out with rich people. If you want to be happy, thin, or creative, befriend folks who display those traits. It has been said that you become like the five people you spend the most time with. So, I recommend that my clients choose their friends–or groups they belong to–very deliberately. Seemingly without effort, people "take on" their friends' beliefs, images, hopes, and habits.

In Chapter 8, I presented the story of Alfred Nobel, who changed his identity by asking himself, "What would I like to be known for by the time I die?" Amazingly, he went from being known as the "merchant of death" to a great humanitarian by focusing on that question. When I was fifteen, shy and depressed, I read about his story. I learned from a book about Alfred Nobel that he had written his "ideal obituary." In it, he wrote what he ideally wanted his kids, friends, and co-workers to say about him at his funeral. It seemed like a good idea, so I did the same. I wrote something like, "Jonathan was a courageous explorer of human potential. He had a deeply loving heart, and affected millions of people with his helpful books and workshops."

When I wrote my ideal obituary, the scenario I described was totally unrealistic. Yet, by writing it down as an imagined vision, it became true over time. I changed my idea of what was possible, and my actions soon followed. Try this exercise for yourself if it appeals to you. For it to have the most significant effect, try reading it once a month. If you're like me, you'll eventually notice that you mysteriously keep moving toward what you wrote down.

Another powerful way to change one's identity is to change what you do regularly. Our self-image often follows from our habitual actions. If you're consistently afraid to try new things, you'll likely think of yourself as fearful. On the other hand, if you skydive and hang glide on a regular basis, you'll think of yourself differently. Therefore, it's important to figure out what actions would help you to experience being a new type of person. For example, I wanted to think of myself as a kind and loving person, so I started volunteering in prisons and feeding people who were hungry. These actions changed how I saw myself.

There are many more ways to change someone's idea of what's possible for themselves. For example, people frequently have one or more beliefs that keep them stuck. If that's the case, therapy or belief-changing exercises can help. My friend, Lion Goodman, has created an extremely powerful belief-changing exercise. It's 18 minutes long and provides a very effective way to change how you feel about yourself and your future. You can find it on my website, along with a lot of other valuable and Free information at this link: https//:EcstasyAsMedicine.com/guidedmeditations

The Basics Of Motivation

Although motivation is a key–if not *the* key–to success in most endeavors, few people know much about it. Fortunately, I used to be a motivational speaker, so I was motivated to learn a lot about it! One misconception many people have about motivation is that you need only become motivated once–and it should last. That's like saying you should only need to eat one meal, which should last for the rest of the year. Motivation usually fades over time, so it must be replenished on occasion.

Another misconception is that you don't need a *system* to stay motivated; you only need a goal you desire. Whatever your goal is, you'll likely face many obstacles before achieving any genuinely worthwhile goal. Consequently, you'll need some method or system to help you stay motivated over a long period. Strong willpower can't compete with a good system for staying motivated. Fortunately, staying consistently motivated is a specialty of mine, so in this and the next chapter, I'll briefly describe some key concepts and methods.

In the wonderful book, "Atomic Habits," James Clear says there are some fundamental ways to approach anything you want to stay motivated to do. Here are a few of his suggestions:

Make it *obvious*. For example, put up post-it notes reminding you of your intention.

Make it *easy*. If you're going to start meditating, begin with 5 minutes instead of an hour

Make it *satisfying*. If you like being in a sauna, do that after you exercise at the gym.

Make it *supported*. Find a friend or a group of people who support what you hope to do or accomplish.

Use the power of *pain and avoidance*. Give yourself a conse-quence if you don't do what you feel would make your life better.

For a book I edited many years ago, I wanted to interview Ram Dass, the spiritual teacher who got kicked out of Harvard with Timothy Leary for doing LSD experiments in the 1960s. Unfortunately, Ram Dass was unresponsive to my letters asking for an interview. However, I knew a system for staying motivated. I put reminders in my calendar to write him every week. The notes I wrote were quick and easy to do. I had a friend check on me periodically to ensure I did something every week to get Ram Dass' attention. Finally, I made a vow that I could only eat ice cream once I got an interview. After 9 *months* of consistent effort, Ram Dass finally called me. Here's how the conversation went.

RD: Hi, this is Ram Dass. Is this Jonathan?

JR: Yes! I'm so glad to hear from you!

RD: Well, I see you've been trying to reach me for a while, so I just wanted to tell you that I don't do interviews like this anymore. I just get too many requests, so I finally just had to say no to any more interviews to focus on my charity work.

JR: Okay, I'm disappointed, but I understand. Thank you for personally telling me.

RD: …However, I've never seen anybody as persistent as you. According to my secretary, you have written to me 36 times, made several phone calls, and even had some friends talk to me about you doing an interview…so my question is, "Are you on a mission from God or are you a complete lunatic?"

JR: Well, when I feel something is important enough, I don't let a little fear and resistance interfere with moving forward–so I guess you could say I'm on a mission from God.

RD: Okay, you sound a bit like me. Let's do the interview…

At the time, I had a compelling story as to why an interview with Ram Dass was so important. I figured other spiritual leaders would soon follow if he'd grant me an interview. It ended up being true; I eventually got to interview everyone from the late Mother Teresa, Wayne Dyer, and M. Scott Peck, to living teachers such as Deepak Chopra and the Dalai Lama. That's another lesson on the path to supercharged motivation. You need to frequently go over your *reason* as to why something is so important to you. If you want peace of mind, or if you want to overcome your depression, write a short essay you can read every night that explains *why* this is critical to your life. If you feel meditating or exercising regularly will help with your goals, write about *how* they will help and why you're committed to being consistent. Periodically replenishing your motivation in this way can be easy to do and very effective.

You have probably heard that we do things to avoid pain and gain pleasure. However, it would be more accurate to say we do things to avoid what we *think* will lead to pain–or what we think will soon or eventually lead to pleasure. What does that mean in the real world? It means that even though exercising may be painful in the immediate moment, we do it because the pain of not exercising may strike us as even more painful. Likewise, going to work may not be pleasurable in the short term, but in the long run, taking care of your family's needs feels good. Therefore, to make significant changes in your life, it's helpful to link massive pain to your old behavior, and lots of pleasure to habits that lead to a new way of being. Fortunately, the 19th-century writer, Charles Dickens, created a story about just how to do this. It was called, "A Christmas Carol."

In Dicken's story, Ebenezer Scrooge changes overnight from a mean and miserly man to one that's generous and kind. How did it happen? First, a "ghost" visited him to show him how his behavior had caused himself and the people he cared about massive amounts of pain in the past. Then, a second ghost showed him how his way of being was causing him massive amounts of pain in his present life. Finally, a third ghost showed him how, if he didn't change his ways, he'd be dead, and everyone would be celebrating. With that much pain associated with his old behavior, Scrooge changed his ways.

To use this powerful technique, sometimes called "The Dicken's Pattern," just write about how a specific behavior or way of being caused you (or is causing you) considerable pain. Be specific and graphic. Don't say, "My fear of going on airplanes means I don't travel much." Instead, detail all the specific great adventures you've missed out on in the past and are now missing because you haven't gotten over your airplane trauma. Once you've linked a lot of pain to your previous limitations, write about how proud of yourself and wonderful it will be when you get free of your previous restrictions. Make that envisioning part of the essay as specific, graphic, and as inspiring as you can possibly make it. Then, read your essay regularly to stay inspired to do what's necessary to transform long term. I've used this method many times, and although it's initially hard to do, it works really well.

Motivation, identity, and integration are all interrelated. If you don't envision a "new you," it will be hard to stick to new behaviors that lead in that direction. If you don't stick to new behaviors that you learned would be helpful, you won't integrate your insights into your daily life. Change takes work. It takes the right experiences, information, guidance, and techniques for lasting change to occur. The good news is that you now have all the ingredients. Still, I want to share with you a couple more techniques for staying motivated. These methods will blow you away. You'll find them thoroughly explained in the next chapter…

CHAPTER 13

THE SURE-FIRE WAYS TO
STAY MOTIVATED

"A lot of people know what to do, but few people do what they know."

— Tony Robbins, author & speaker

When a person comes to me for MDMA or traditional talk therapy, they usually have a long history of dealing with an inner challenge. When someone has physical pain in their body that persists, they'll often seek a doctor's help within a month. On the other hand, people will usually wait years or decades before seeking help when dealing with trauma, anxiety, or depression. That's the bad news. The good news is that they can still be helped, but after an initial transformative experience, most people will need ongoing support. Although old conditioning can often be seen through in a day, it doesn't just disappear after many years of repetition. For ongoing transformation to occur, new behaviors must be established and made into habits.

Early in my career, I realized clients needed ongoing support for establishing new habits, but they frequently couldn't afford to pay for therapy week after week. Yet, without support, they often fell into the same old patterns that created their suffering in the first place. What to do?

I decided to seek new ways clients could get the support they needed without paying me to keep them moving forward. Eventually, my exploration led to the creation of the "ICAN Method" which stands for **I**nternal **C**ontract **A**nd **N**urturance Method. This technique helps people stay motivated for long periods of time to create new habits–without having to keep seeing a therapist. In addition, it costs virtually nothing, only takes five minutes a week, and is practically 100% effective when used as described. Before going into the details of the ICAN Method, explaining some of its underlying principles is important.

First, as stated in the previous chapter, people do things to avoid pain and gain pleasure. Unfortunately, many things that are good for us are immediately difficult, and things that are bad for us (heroin, donuts, etc.) usually feel pretty good initially. This aspect of the human condition makes change hard to maintain. We may say we'll go to the gym three times in the next week, but then we often break our promise to ourselves. After breaking our word to ourselves (and others), we acquire weak "promise muscles." By that, I mean our promises to ourselves and others often fail to be backed up by action. So, we may say to ourselves, "I'm going to do that trauma release exercise I learned," but in the back of our mind, a voice says, "Bullshit! You rarely follow through." This pattern needs to change, and a whole new technique is called for in order for it to change.

Contracts are used in business for a simple reason: they work. In the ICAN Method, you write a contract that lists a few items you commit to complete within one week. Contracts are always just for one week. This is because you know what your upcoming week will be like. During busy weeks, you might put fewer things on your contract that you commit to doing. In addition, by writing a contract for just a week, you can readjust your contract to the needs of a given week.

There are three things that make contracts a powerful force for changing people's behavior. First, is accountability. All contracts have some form of accountability to verify the parties involved actually did what they said they would do. In the ICAN Method, you can be accountable to a mate, a friend, a coach, or a therapist. Preferably, the person you're accountable to is also using *you* as an accountability partner for *their* contract—but that is not a requirement. Second, all contracts have a deadline. You need to know when the contract is up so any violations can be determined at a precise time. And lastly, all contracts have clearly defined consequences if people don't do what the contract says they should do.

Finding an appropriate consequence to give yourself can be tricky when you violate your contract. If you make the consequence too big, you won't abide by it when you fail—and the whole contract idea collapses. However, if you make the pain for contract violations too small, it won't potentially motivate you to do what you said you'd do. After a whole lot of trial and error, I only found one consequence that worked extremely well. It was a penalty small enough that people would truly implement it if they broke their contract agreements. Yet, at the same time, the consequence was impactful enough that they'd do almost anything to avoid it. Before I tell you what this penalty is, you should know a few things about it:

It is not illegal

It takes only a minute to implement

It works even when you're positively sure it won't work

It works immediately, and it even works after many years of using it

It has slight variations depending on what country you live in

So, are you curious? The penalty is very simple: anytime you fail to do an item on your contract, you take the equivalent of $1.00 and rip it up or throw it in the garbage. That's it. This is a lot more impactful than you might imagine. I've had clients who snorted $20,000 of cocaine a month stop their habit to avoid ripping up $1.00. If you don't live in the US, you might not be able to rip up the equivalent of $1.00, but you can throw away a similar amount of money in the garbage. You can't give this money away because that would not be painful. Instead, you want to tell your brain that there is a clear and definitive price to pay when you don't do what you promised. Astonishingly, the threat of ripping up or throwing away a dollar is enough to change people's behavior. I was skeptical too, but after using this method with over 10,000 people, I know it works.

At the end of the one-week contract date, a friend, mate, guide, or therapist holds you accountable for the items on your contract. For each item you failed to finish by the completion time, you must rip up or throw away the equivalent of $1.00 US. Some of the things on your contract, such as exercising or meditating each day, may be hard to do. Yet, destroying money is very painful. When you must decide between ripping up a dollar and meditating for 30 minutes, you'll likely choose to meditate. From such "decision points," new behaviors are established. Moreover, even if you choose to rip up $1.00, you're still keeping your word. Gradually, your "word" or promise to yourself grows stronger as you keep to your written commitments.

To give you a better understanding of this method, I'll show you a recent contract a client wrote up during their integration session with me:

I, Derrick, agree to complete the following items by this time next week:

1. Meditate every day for at least 20 minutes
2. Exercise 3 times for at least 45 minutes each time
3. Put on a post-it note the technique I plan to focus on for the day to help me handle any anxiety that arises.
4. Read a minimum of 20 pages from the book, "The Body Keeps the Score"

5. Take out the garbage by 3 pm Monday

For each item I fail to complete by one week from today, I agree to rip up (or throw away) $1.00

signature)_____(date and time)_____

Notice that most of the items on Derrick's contract refer to things that will assist with overcoming his anxiety. However, taking out the garbage is a different type of task. It's perfectly acceptable to put items on your contract that make your finances, relationships, or life work better if you have a clear way of determining whether they are done.

When writing a weekly contract, I tell my clients to write SMART goals. That is, make your contractual items **S**pecific, **M**easureable, **A**chieveable, **R**elevant, and **T**ime-bound. One client learned this lesson when he simply wrote on his contract, "Go to the gym three times." Well, he forgot about the gym until 30 minutes before his contract deadline. So, he drove to the gym, walked in, walked out, walked in, walked out, walked in, walked out and technically he kept his contract to go to the gym three times. With money on the line, people get very sneaky. However, for his next contract, he added that he needed to "exercise at the gym for at least 45 minutes" each time he went. Over time, you learn to write more precise, helpful contracts, and relevant to doing the key behaviors that will have the most impact on your life.

I tell my clients to start slow when first using the ICAN Method. Simply ask yourself, "*What are the most important things for me to do this week to take great care of myself and move forward in my life?*" Begin the process with two or three contract items per week. Feel free to add more items as you get the hang of it. Once you've written the contract, sign it, print out a copy for yourself, and place it where you'll see it every day–like your bathroom mirror. Then, email your accountability partner a copy and clarify how you'll be in touch when the contract deadline arises.

While the ICAN Method is extremely effective, I've found that people are only consistent with it if they have someone they can be accountable to. This need not take much time. In fact, with my accountability partner, Dan, we schedule a five-minute call every Thursday afternoon at 5:00. Our conversation sounds like this:

JR: Howdy Dan. How'd you do on your contract last week?

DAN: I got everything done, and I emailed you my contract for next week five minutes ago.

JR: Great job. As for me, I missed one item. I forgot to meditate one day. You'll notice that on this week's contract—which I just emailed you, I'm going to allow myself to miss one day of meditation during the week.

DAN: Good idea. Did you rip up a dollar yet?

JR: Yes, and it was painful. But it's worth it. It's helping me be a lot more consistent with meditation than I used to be.

DAN: Good to hear. I'll talk to you next Thursday.

JR: Okay, have a great week.

That's it. Knowing that someone is holding you accountable for your contract is the magic that makes this idea work so well. With the ICAN Method, in five minutes a week you can dramatically increase your motivation toward what is truly important to you. All you need to do to get started is to find a friend, mate, co-worker, coach, or therapist who is willing to hold you accountable at the same time each week. Although it's not necessary that they also create a contract each week, it can be a bonus if accountability is a two-way street.

Besides the threat of throwing away money, the ICAN Method works so well because it forces people to clearly decide what they *must* do each week. We all have things we'd *like* to do, but we frequently don't do things that fall into the "would like to" category. However, once we put something in the "must category," our attitude shifts. For example, no matter how busy you are and no matter how inconvenient it is, you always find a toilet when you need one. Finding a toilet is a *must* in your brain. Failure to find a toilet is not an option. Therefore, you can go decades without failing to get to a needed toilet. Amazing. That's the power of clarifying what must occur before a given deadline. The ICAN Method is a simple way to tap into this power.

The ICAN Method can even take on magical qualities. I've been doing it for 30 years, and in that time, I've seen what seems like Divine intervention occasionally occur. One memorable example is when I sought to interview Mother Teresa back in 1993. At that time, there was no Internet, so I didn't have a clue as to how to get hold of her. Yet, I had written on my contract, "I will talk to Mother Teresa this week." I went to the local library and discovered that she had created an organization called "The Sisters of Charity." I got a phone number for that organization in India. Then, I gave that number a call.

In 1993, calling and getting through to a phone number in India was about as likely as calling a random number and getting someone on the International Space Station. Yet, it was on my contract to try it, so I dialed the number I had for The Sisters of Charity. To my surprise, a woman with a friendly voice quickly answered the phone. I said, "Hi, my name is Jonathan, and I'm editing a book about how spiritual leaders connect with their Higher Power. I'd like to interview Mother Teresa. Do you know of any way I might be able to talk to her?"

The woman who answered the phone said, "This is Ma. How can I help you?"

I responded, "Ma, might you be able to help connect me with Mother Teresa?"

The woman responded, "Yes, this is Ma."

Then it hit me. This woman who had answered the phone WAS Mother Teresa! I burst into tears. The grace and miracle of calling India and having her answer the phone seemed almost ludicrous. I quickly pulled myself together and began asking her my questions. She was very nice and humble. At one point, I asked her how she meditates, and she said, "I mostly pray, but I know the Dalai Lama knows a lot about meditation. Would you like his phone number?" I assured her that I would love his phone number—which is how I also managed to interview him later on. Finally, I asked Mother Teresa if she was in the habit of answering her organization's phone. She said, "No, I've been too busy, but it rang while I was walking by, and by God's Grace, I hope I can help your readers."

From this and other seemingly miraculous experiences, committing to your contract opens the door to acts of grace entering your life more frequently. Try it, and you'll see what I mean.

Having used the ICAN Method with thousands of people over many years, I know how much certain new behaviors tend to cost over time. For example, if a person wants to start meditating every day, that usually leads to about $2.00 per month of destroyed money. If a person wants to lose 25 pounds, on average, that takes 20 weeks and costs about $4.00. Why so little money? Most weeks, people do all the items they put on their contract to help them lose weight or achieve whatever they desire. Occasionally, they miss something and must throw away a dollar–thus the $4.00 cost before losing 20 pounds. So, it's not about throwing away a large amount of money. The clarity of the contract's terms, accountability, and small penalty work like magic. You'll be amazed at how well it works if you try this for yourself.

If the ICAN Method seems too intense for you or a client, you can always do a "lighter" version. As discussed in the last chapter, joining a group or having friends with similar goals can help people be consistent with new behavior. It doesn't work as well as the ICAN Method, but any support is better than nothing. If you or a client can afford to hire a coach or a therapist for ongoing integration work, that is also a great option. After I lead clients through a journey, they'll often hire me for a biweekly half-hour check-in call to keep them accountable and help them make any adjustments to their ongoing program. Usually, that's all that's needed to keep them moving forward, and since it's only an hour of my time per month, the cost is very reasonable. Clients who get this one hour of continuing professional support per month do incredibly well over time. I highly recommend it for all my journey clients.

The Power of Scheduling

A final technique to stay true to healing activities is the simple act of scheduling them. Nowadays, we're all so busy that we often don't have time to do things that aren't scheduled. So, if you want to make sure you do something, schedule it in your calendar. In fact, schedule the exact time you plan to do a particular activity and how much time you plan to give it. People rarely miss doctor's appointments. Why? Because they are scheduled into their calendar. That's why when I coach people, before the call is over, I make sure they've scheduled exact times for any new behaviors they plan to do. People tend to be very good at following their digital or paper calendar–so take advantage of this fact to improve their (or your) mental health.

Sometimes people resist doing things that are good for their mental health because they see them as less necessary than other activities. They may even feel guilty spending time with friends, meditating, exercising, or other self-care activities. However, if it's scheduled into their calendar, they do it because it's on their schedule! It's as if they're now being required to do something, and since it's a requirement, they can do it guilt-free. We human beings are funny creatures.

Because most people have a long history of making resolutions–then failing to keep them–they may be skeptical that anything can work for them. Indeed, without the help of consistent motivational support, they are very likely to fail. That's why the various motivational techniques in this and the previous chapter are so important to know and practice. MDMA journeys are wonderful, intense, and often transformative, but they aren't sorcery. People must take what they learned from their session and apply it, week after week, into their lives. The ICAN Method, combined with the power of scheduling, are two tools that can turn the word "impossible" into "I'm possible." When people see they can change with the help of these potent methods, it immediately gives them new hope that propels them towards a better life.

CHAPTER 14

THE FUTURE OF MEDICINE THERAPY

"When we are no longer able to change a situation—we are challenged to change ourselves."

—Victor Frankl, holocaust survivor and author

Currently, the future of the world looks rather bleak to many people. There's not much we can do to change the world, but as Victor Frankl points out in the quote above, we can always change ourselves. Now that we've (hopefully) entered an era in which scientific studies begin to determine drug policy, a lot of doors are opening to psychedelics and their potential value to heal. How the future unfolds is always up for grabs. Historically, we've seen the pendulum swing between "all these drugs are horrible" to "all these drugs are amazing" and back again. Yet, never before have so many well-done studies been published that indicate the astonishing value of MDMA and other psychedelics. As time passes, putting the genie back in the bottle will be harder and harder.

MDMA and other psychedelics are not addictive. However, that doesn't mean they can't be abused. Back in 1984, when I saw how powerful MDMA was for curing PTSD, I wondered how people could and would abuse this medicine. The fact that it would be used at parties for all-night dancing never crossed my mind. I've been to a couple of raves. They're fun. Yet, using this sacred medicine to have a good time dancing is like using a laptop as a doorstop. Sure, it works, but there are better uses for a laptop—and there are better uses for MDMA. Once this medicine gets FDA approval, a lot more "off-label" experimentation will occur. That will eventually lead to new and creative ways MDMA is used and abused.

In a conversation with Rick Doblin (the founder of MAPS) in July of 2023, he said he hopes MDMA will be made entirely legal by 2035. In the meantime, it's important to stay informed of the changing legal status of MDMA in your country. Once the FDA approves it as a medically prescribed drug in the U.S.A, there will be a lot of pressure on insurance companies to pay for the treatment of PTSD. Mr. Doblin hopes that some insurance companies will pay for the rather expensive treatment immediately, while others will eventually join in when they see it saves them money in the long run. Yet, precisely what will happen and how insurance companies will handle the newly approved treatment is still up in the air. MAPS is doing what it can to convince insurance companies to pay for anyone who might benefit from this type of therapy—not just PTSD patients. Getting insurance companies involved is important because the treatment will likely cost significantly over $10,000.

To reduce the cost of therapy, MAPS is exploring alternatives to the model they championed of doing three MDMA sessions with two therapists. One possibility would be to do group therapy sessions with MDMA. Another option would be to have clients use fewer sessions. As Rick told me, "Not everybody's going to need three sessions; ...some people can need just one or two." I believe most people will only need a single MDMA session to get really good results. The reason why the MAPS protocol decided to have three sessions is that, according to Rick, "Our approach was how do we get the best results? It wasn't what's the least expensive way we can get just barely good enough results." In addition, to get FDA approval, Rick Doblin told me, "We decided we needed to work with the hardest cases." However, in the future, most people wanting MDMA therapy won't be people who have suffered from extreme symptoms of PTSD for many years. Your average client will be in much better shape than that when requesting MDMA therapy.

As an underground therapist, I aim to train people to do high-quality MDMA therapy at a reasonable price. In my conversation with Rick Doblin, I told him I was hoping to get the therapists I train to offer this therapy for as little as $500. At that price, many people might be interested in trying something that's proven to be quick, effective, and leads to lasting change. Rick was excited about my personal mission and stated, "Well, I think this idea of a single session costing in the neighborhood of $500 is a tremendous situation and will be something that many millions of people will want." Hopefully, after FDA approval, there will be enough therapists and guides offering this type of therapy at a price point many folks can afford.

Another future scenario for MDMA is how it will be mixed with other drugs. MDMA has long been combined with other psychedelics to create interesting and possibly valuable therapeutic combinations. However, it needs to be stated that combining drugs, especially illegal street drugs, can sometimes lead to unpredictable and dangerous results. Nevertheless, MDMA has a long history of being used in combination with other psychedelics. For example, MDMA in combination with LSD is called "candy flipping," and many people think it's the most incredible high in the world. MDMA plus psilocybin mushrooms is called "hippie flipping," and it has many enthusiastic adherents. I've tried both, and they were both great–like mixing chocolate and peanut butter. But are they of therapeutic value? Initial studies show promise, but it's way too early to tell. Since psilocybin and MDMA tend to last about the same length (4 to 6 hours), it's more likely that "hippie flipping" will be more actively studied than MDMA in combination with LSD.

I have limited experience in combining MDMA with psilocybin–for both myself and my work with others. However, I've noticed a few things. First, many factors influence the results. There are the traditional considerations of set and setting, along with the additional factors, such as:

The order in which you take the mushrooms and MDMA

How long do you wait in between dosing

The dose of each medicine

Whether the MDMA is, in fact, MDMA and not something else

Unique biological and psychological factors

Because you can vary so many elements, it's hard to make any definitive statement as to what "hippie flipping" does. But, in my experience, I've found that a combination of a normal dose of MDMA (120 mg) and a low dose of mushrooms (1/2 to 1 gram) leads to a very enjoyable and therapeutic effect. At such a dose, I've seen people get the best of both worlds: love, serenity, joy, and an ability to see things differently. If a person takes a higher dose of mushrooms (2 to 4 grams), they can still have an amazing experience, but rational talking about issues becomes much more challenging. Eventually, studies will be done to ascertain the optimal dosage of MDMA plus psilocybin for dealing with various psychological issues. Till then, you'll just have to take your best guess.

MDMA has also been mixed with other drugs I briefly discussed in Chapter 4. MDMA combined with Ketamine is called "Kitty flipping," but it's not known for its therapeutic potential. Since marijuana is commonly used nowadays, some folks combine it with MDMA at some point in their journey. Many people report they like to smoke or eat marijuana towards the end of an MDMA journey. They say this tends to prolong the MDMA experience and make the comedown softer. Once again, there is little research about mixing drugs, but the prudent thing to do is to be very careful when doing so. People can sometimes get in trouble because combining drugs can sometimes lead to unexpected and unpleasant effects that are unpredictable.

Recent research in mental health has shown that we have an epidemic of loneliness. Studies show that people who feel lonely have many negative health effects from social isolation.[9]

According to the CDC, social isolation significantly increases a person's risk of premature death from all causes, a risk that may rival those of smoking, obesity, and physical inactivity. In addition, social isolation is associated with a 50% increased risk of dementia. Of course, one potential remedy for loneliness is taking MDMA to connect with others in a group setting. This has been done frequently since the 1980s at dance parties, raves, and music festivals. Yet, such venues are not attempting to be therapeutic or aimed at helping people connect one-to-one with each other. In the future, there will likely be various types of gatherings that use MDMA (instead of alcohol) as a social lubricant.

Recently, I've been invited to gatherings where several friends and I have taken MDMA together to connect on a deeper level. I've been struck by how satisfying and healing these gatherings have been. When MDMA becomes a legally prescribed medicine, I imagine there will be a lot of gatherings where folks take MDMA as a remedy for the disconnection that ails modern society. As a friend of mine likes to say, "Extraordinary times call for extraordinary pleasures." MDMA may just be what the doctor orders to combat the increasing isolation of our current culture.

While MDMA is a great medicine, it's not the only game in town. In the last few years, some MDMA substitutes have been invented that

---

[9] https://www.cdc.gov/aging/publications/features/lonely-older-adults.html

mimic the effects of MDMA–but are perfectly legal in most countries. Before purchasing such products, always make sure you know the legal and safety status of whatever you might try to consume.

In the United States, there is one "MDMA substitute" I like that you can buy, and it's quite good. It's called "Velvet Crush." This supplement is legal, but it does have some Yohimbe in it, and Yohimbe is contraindicated for people with high blood pressure and certain other health conditions. You can Google Yohimbe to learn more. If you'd like to try *Velvet Crush*, you can call a store named *Twisted Thistle Apothecary*. They are in Oakland, California. Their number is 510-644-3727. It costs $22 for two pills; they'll even mail it to you for a little extra charge. If you can't find a good MDMA source, or you're worried about the illegality of it where you live, *Velvet Crush* can be a good alternative. I take just one pill when I've used it, but some people take two. It lasts about 5 hours.

If you're eager to explore the effects of some of the cutting-edge legal products on yourself, I can make some suggestions. In recent years, many companies have come out with products that are a combination of many nootropics. Nootropics are supplements that help you feel alert and good by inundating you with a lot of healthy brain food. The best-known nootropic is caffeine, but many other substances are safe and effective, and when combined in nootropic "stacks," they can make you feel extremely good and loving. Many of my friends and I regularly alter our moods with various "smart pills." Having been an avid follower of such supplementation, I've been impressed with how much better they are getting over the last few years. If you ever saw the movie or TV show, Limitless, you can understand the possibilities inherent in such products.

If you're eager to explore the world of nootropics, I can make some recommendations.

If you go to:

https://neurohacker.com/findinghappiness ...you can find out all about some cutting-edge nootropics. In fact, if you use the coupon code, "FindingHappiness" you'll get 10% off your order (and I'll get a 5% kickback).

I also like the products on this website:

https://nootopia.com/

...They have a lot of innovative supplements that can help you feel euphoria, energized, and/or joyous. Since people react differently to various formulas, I suggest trying a starter package where you get a small amount of different nootropic stacks. On their website, they have you fill out a short survey so they can match you with a formula that meets your unique needs and specifications. The effects of some of these legal supplements can be as powerful as MDMA. However, only through experimentation will you know their exact effects on you.

In the future, individuals will have varying levels of interest in exploring the procession of legal and illegal substances that will appear on the world market. That's perfectly understandable. However, talk therapy will increasingly rely on various medicines and supplements to enhance therapeutic outcomes. In addition, studies are now being conducted to test if various nootropics can help people integrate what they have experienced in psychedelic therapy. It's too early to tell in the research, but my experience would suggest that some nootropics can indeed help keep people motivated, happy, and open to new learning. The popularity of antidepressants–taking a pill to treat a condition–would suggest the future looks bright for nootropics to help people integrate therapeutic insights.

Some of the latest research about psychedelics has pointed to a "critical learning period" associated with MDMA and other psychedelics.

In essence, this research shows that various psychedelics help make the brain more open to new learning and new behaviors for various lengths of time.[10]

As researchers study this important phenomenon, they may discover or create even better drugs that help people open to accelerated learning and change. However, before trying the latest supplement or drug being touted by the media, I encourage you to display caution when putting any substance in your body that has unknown or unsubstantiated effects. In my experience, I've found that some nootropics and all psychedelics I've taken seem to turbo-charge my ability to be insightful, and intuitive, and change unproductive behavior. Yet, every person and every body reacts differently to these medicines. Your job is to be as informed as possible about the potential advantages and disadvantages of any medicine you put into your unique body. All that being said, I'm excited to see what future studies indicate about various supplements that can increase our ability to learn and change at an accelerated rate.

Hopefully, the information I've supplied here is enough to give you a direction and starting point. I'm not trying to give you a full account of what's available. Instead, I aim to introduce you to this fast-developing field of using nootropics and psychedelics as an adjunct to therapy. For better or worse, there are a lot of options to explore. Many people I know "mix and match" supplements and psychedelics of various kinds until they find a combination that suits their needs. Once a person finds some pills that seem to have a truly positive effect on their mood and focus—and are also devoid of adverse side effects—they have a friend for life. The future of therapy may require a variety of pills and tools that help people overcome their various psychological challenges.

---

[10] https://www.nature.com/articles/s41586-023-06204-3

How to Evaluate a Substance or Supplement's Value

To know if a specific supplement or drug is genuinely your friend, you need to be able to clearly see its precise effects on your life. Supplements affect people in different ways--in the same way that alcohol is a fun way to relax for some people and an addictive hell for others. To identify if a particular supplement or drug is a "friend" to you, I've devised a simple method. What follows are six questions to help you evaluate how a supplement affects the quality of your daily life--and whether it might be useful to explore more frequently.

Does This Supplement Bring You Closer to People or Help Isolate You?

Research shows that the number one factor in creating a life of happiness is the quality of your relationships. Therefore, it's essential to question whether the supplements or drugs you use are bringing you closer to people. Unfortunately, 300 Facebook friends do not equal one truly good friend you trust will always be there for you. If "love and connection" are a top value for you, it's important to consider if anything you put in your body is genuinely leading to quality connections.

Does This Supplement Bring You Closer to Inner Peace or Make You Feel More Stressed?

By asking if a specific supplement helps move you towards more peace, you can make better decisions about when and how much to use them. I take a formula from Nootopia.com about twice a week that makes me feel a deep sense of peace. On other days, I don't take this formula because I don't want to get addicted to it or start to depend on it for feeling good. Each body and person is unique, so you must be honest with yourself and ascertain when something is helpful and when an unhealthy dependency might develop.

Does This Supplement Add Depth/Joy, and Happiness to Your Life, or Move You Towards Superficiality and Anxiety?

This question can apply not only to supplements and drugs, but also to any activity you engage in. For example, does being on Facebook or watching Netflix add to your happiness, or do they just fill up time? Does drinking two cups of coffee daily bring you more joy and depth, or just get you feeling speedy and productive? The answers will be different for each person. Ultimately, we all want a life filled with depth, meaning, and happiness, but our culture points us more toward productivity than depth. By asking this question, you can evaluate how a specific supplement or activity affects you at this point in your life.

Does This Supplement Make You More Compassionate, Kind, and Loving, Or More Self-Absorbed?

One of the wonderful things about MDMA is it almost always points people toward greater feelings of love and compassion. Drugs such as LSD and Ketamine are not known for doing that, but they can serve other purposes. When considering a new drug's use, it's important to consider its potential downsides. For example, I've known people who take LSD and Ketamine a lot, and it has always looked like they started becoming more self-absorbed. Had they asked themselves this question, they may have noticed they are moving in a direction that may not be healthy for their life. If love and compassion are truly as important as we say they are, then we should see if the supplements we use are helping us toward that end.

Does This Supplement Improve Your Health or Negatively Impact Your Health?

An obvious consideration when taking any supplement is how it affects your body. For some people, even if they take a bunch of vitamins to help recover from MDMA, something in their body has difficulty with it. On the other hand, I almost always feel great the day after taking Ecstasy. I've said it before, and I'll say it again—everyone is different.

Listen to your body, not your mind that might say, "I want it no matter what." If you try a supplement a couple of times and it clearly stresses your body, try something else. If your body has a difficult time with all the supplements you try, see your doctor to see why that might be the case.

Does This Supplement Make You A Wiser Person or More Immature?

To a large extent, whether a supplement makes you wiser or not depends on how you use it. Some people use marijuana as a sacred herb that helps them meditate, gain insight, and connect with the heart of humanity. Other people use marijuana to get wasted, munch Doritos, and watch Wheel of Fortune. So, when considering if a supplement makes you wiser, you must consider two things. First, what does this drug or supplement seem to do to me? For example, alcohol makes some people more heart oriented, but it makes other people turn into belligerent jerks. Second, you need to consider how well you habitually use a certain medicine. Do you create a sacred set and setting or use a certain supplement just for relief? As you consider this question, you can see if a supplement has a deeper value to you.

The Issue of Tolerance.

People often build up a tolerance to supplements that they take frequently. Take caffeine, for example. If you've never had a cup of coffee, that first cup will likely make you feel like you can run a marathon. However, if you drink coffee frequently, you may need more and more for it to have any effect on you. Because tolerance can occur so quickly with many medicines, having a few you know work for you is helpful. That way, you can avoid taking and depending on any single supplement to benefit you. In my case, I drink coffee twice a week, take other supplements once or twice a week, and take nothing once or twice a week. I've been doing that for years, and this approach has helped me stay sensitive to the various things I ingest.

Many people who have taken a lot of MDMA have found the effects become less over time. Once again, their body has grown used to the medicine, leading to its lesser effect. When people tell me they don't feel MDMA as much as they used to, I suggest they lay off that medicine for a while. In fact, I think that it's a good thing that people build-up tolerance towards MDMA and other drugs. It's your body's way of saying, "Don't become dependent on this or take it so casually." It's always a good idea to listen to your body.

We live in a fast-changing world. It's easy to get overwhelmed with all that's going on. Fortunately, we are amid a drug and supplement renaissance. More medicines and mind-altering substances are now available to the common person than ever before in history. If we can use these mind aids responsibly, we can better handle the unique challenges of the times we live in. Through careful personal exploration, in combination with scientific studies, the future of therapy looks brighter than it has ever been. Hopefully, we'll be able to use these new mind medicines and supplements to better meet our needs and heal our wounds.

CONCLUSION

"Find ecstasy in life; the mere sense of living is joy enough."

— Emily Dickinson, author

A "conclusion" allows me to summarize what I think are the most important things to remember and get from this book. Here you go: MDMA is a sacred and amazing medicine if used properly. But, like anything in life, you get out of it what you put into it. If you have a clear intention to use MDMA to cure your PTSD, depression, anxiety, or relationship issues, this medicine can greatly help. You may (or may not) be able to treat a long-standing condition in a day, but you'll likely see enough improvement to be inspired to keep moving forward on your healing journey. If healing is your intention, I encourage you to find a therapist or guide who can help you.

In my journeys with hundreds of people, I've learned that we have many intriguing ways we get twisted up in knots. However, we also have strong spirits that yearn for release from our obstacles. MDMA-assisted therapy is most effective if you understand how to set yourself up for success. A friend of mine that leads journeys says the success of a session is 1/3rd from the dedication of the explorer, 1/3rd from the effect of the medicine, and 1/3rd from the facilitator's skill. I agree. If you set things up well, you'll likely be well rewarded. Of course, just as aspirin doesn't work for everyone, a small percentage of people don't resonate with this medicine. However, rest assured that there's an excellent chance the results you get from a well set-up MDMA session is likely to surprise you.

Many years ago, I visited a famous guru in India named Papaji. As I entered his crowded living room, I was surprised to have him immediately point to me and tell me to sit before him. A bit nervous, I did as I was told. As I sat before Papaji, he looked at me intently with his beaming, joyous eyes. Finally, he asked me, "Who are you?"

Innocently, I replied, "I'm Jonathan Robinson."

Papaji and the many people watching my exchange with him began to snicker and laugh at my answer. I was very embarrassed and thought to myself, "Well, I guess that was the wrong answer."

Finally, Papaji offered compassionately, "No, who are you *really?*"

I replied, "I'm a spiritual seeker." Papaji silently shook his head, indicating *that* wasn't the answer he was looking for.

I tried again. "I'm a writer." Again, a "no" response. I tried answering with various identities: a man, a husband, an ego, an American, but none of my answers were greeted affirmatively. Finally, I decided to stop digging my hole deeper with my answers and just silently look into his sparkling eyes. Suddenly, I felt a churning in my chest, accompanied by some fear. I surrendered to this churning, and before I knew it, a tremendous wave of emotion hit me. The feeling was one of complete, unbounded, infinite love. I began to sob in Papaji's lap.

As I cried in Papaji's lap, he patted me gently on the head and said words I will never forget. He said, "This love you feel now is who you really are, and your *job* in life is to find your way back to it any way you can." To the best of my ability, those words have helped steer me throughout my life since then.

When I guide people on their journeys, I see great beauty and love in every person's essence. The sacred medicine known as Ecstasy is an incredible gift to unlock the human spirit and heart. Perhaps more than ever, we need helpers to find our way back to love. When we connect with our essence of love, it leads to healing. When we heal ourselves, we can better serve those we love–and become a healing force in the world.

© BRILLIANT ENTERPRISES 1970

YOUR ILLNESS LICENSE
HAS EXPIRED —
REPORT BACK TO HEALTH
IMMEDIATELY!

POT-SHOTS NO. 156

Ashleigh
Brilliant

ACKNOWLEDGMENTS

I've had many people teach me about psychedelics, love, and healing. High on that very long list are the folks I dedicated this book to. Yet, I also want to acknowledge my wife, Kirsten and Dr. Deborah Bice for their loving support. I want to thank Brian Tom O'Connor for help with our podcast, Hitch McDermid for editing assistance, and Amir Giles for his great support with my online MDMA training program. Thanks to all of you. It takes a village to write a book; you're my village.

ABOUT THE AUTHOR

Jonathan Robinson is a psychotherapist, best-selling author of 14 books, and a professional speaker from Northern California. He has reached over 200 million people around the world with his practical methods, and his work has been translated into 47 languages. Mr. Robinson has made numerous appearances on *The Oprah Show* and CNN, as well as other national TV talk shows.

Jonathan is the author of several bestsellers, including *The Enlightenment Project* and *Communication Miracles for Couples*. He is also the co-host of the popular podcast *Awareness Explorers*. Jonathan regularly speaks at psychedelic conferences and Fortune 500 companies such as Google, Microsoft, and Apple. He is known for his highly entertaining presentations filled with practical information.

To get more information about Jonathan's MDMA facilitator training, go to MDMAtraining.net. If you'd like to contact Jonathan, or receive free information on MDMA updates and how to avoid bad psychedelic trips, go to XTCasMedicine.com.

Made in the USA
Monee, IL
19 October 2023

44865313R00098